INSECTS

OF

NEW ZEALAND

BRIAN PARKINSON
PHOTOGRAPHS BY DON HORNE

Dedications

To Alison Henry, with much affection
　　　– Brian Parkinson

*I'd like to dedicate my photographic work to my wife,
Gwen, and my family and grandchildren for the fun
times of discovery in the field*
　　　– Don Horne

Acknowledgements

Marie-Claude Lariviere, Landcare Research (cicadas)
Grace Hall, Landcare Research (grasshoppers)
Dave Towns, Department of Conservation, Auckland (mayflies)
Terry Hitchings, Canterbury Museum (mayflies)
Barry Donovan, DSIR, Lincoln (native bees)
Chris Green, Department of Conservation, Auckland (beetles)
Trevor Crosby, Landcare Research (various)
Graeme Ramsay (weta and stick insects)
Pat Dale (flies and wasps)

First published in 2007 by New Holland Publishers (NZ) Ltd
Auckland • Sydney • London • Cape Town

www.newhollandpublishers.co.nz

218 Lake Road, Northcote, Auckland, New Zealand
14 Aquatic Drive, Frenchs Forest, NSW 2086, Australia
86–88 Edgware Road, London W2 2EA, United Kingdom
80 McKenzie Street, Cape Town 8001, South Africa

Copyright © 2007 in text: Brian Parkinson
Copyright © 2007 in photography: Don Horne, unless otherwise specified
Copyright © 2007 New Holland Publishers (NZ) Ltd
ISBN 978-1-86966-151-9

Managing editor: Matt Turner
Editor: Brian O'Flaherty
Consultant: John Early, Auckland Museum
Design: Punaromia
Illustrations: Cuni de Graaf

A catalogue record for this book is available from the National Library of
New Zealand

Colour reproduction by Pica Digital Pte Ltd, Singapore
Printed by Times Offset (M) Sdn Bhd, Malaysia

10 9 8 7 6 5 4 3 2 1

Front cover photograph: katydid (*Caedicia simplex*)
Back cover photograph: yellow admiral (*Bassaris itea*)
Spine photograph: large-spotted ladybird (*Harmonia conformis*)
Title page photograph: large striped carpet (*Asaphodes clarata*)

Contents

Introduction

What is an insect?

Insects form a major part of the large assembly of animals known as the arthropods, which means 'jointed legs'. Besides insects, the major groups of arthropods include the arachnids (spiders, scorpions, ticks and mites); the crustaceans (slaters, crabs, crayfish and others); and the myriapods and diplopods, which we know better as the millipedes and centipedes. Arthropods are invertebrates, which means that they lack a backbone. Instead, they have a soft internal body encased within a protective jointed casing, or exoskeleton. Insects differ from all other arthropods in having only three pairs of legs and a three-part body, consisting of a head, thorax and abdomen. Spiders, with which they are most often confused, have by contrast four pairs of legs and a two-part body and are never winged. Insect anatomy is covered in more detail on page 8.

Naming and classifying insects

Insects, like all other animals, are identified according to the principles of taxonomy, which is the scientific classification into hierarchical groups known as taxa (singular = taxon). The system in use today was devised by the Swedish physician and amateur botanist Carl von Linné, better known as Carolus Linnaeus, who lived from 1707 to 1778.

Linnaeus felt that the taxonomic system prevailing in his time was unwieldy and inaccurate, so set out to devise a more efficient one. His *Systema Naturae*, based in large part on the ranking structure then in use in the Swedish army and first published in 1735, had three main objectives:

- to create a system to classify every organism then known and yet to be discovered;
- to get this system universally accepted;
- to make this system internationally useable by adopting Latin, a transnational language then understood by all scientists.

Auckland tree weta, male.

Although the use of Latin is not so strictly followed nowadays, with other languages, even Maori, often favoured, the general principles still prevail, and the Linnaean system is still used. It is a rigorous system and one worth learning about, because it increases our understanding of insects. The major taxon to which all animals belong is the kingdom Animalia. Within the Animalia are several subdivisions called phyla (singular = phylum), one of which is the Arthropoda. And so it continues down to species level. The six taxa below the kingdom level in order of rank are phylum, class, order, family, genus and species. If you are the type of person who finds mnemonics handy, a useful one to help you remember the sequence of the taxa is 'Please Carry On For Goodness Sake'.

Using the example of the Auckland tree weta (*Hemideina thoracica*; see photo opposite), the table below shows how the Linnaean system is used to identify a single species.

Kingdom: Animalia (animals)
Phylum: Arthropoda (arthropods)
Class: Insecta (insects)
Order: Orthoptera (grasshoppers and weta)
Family: Anostostomatidae (weta)
Genus: *Hemideina* (tree weta)
Species: *thoracica* (Auckland tree weta)

With the recent addition of the newly discovered African order, Mantophasmatodea, scientists now recognise 30 orders within the Insecta. The springtails (Collembola), proturans (Protura) and diplurans (Diplura) were once considered insects but are now classed as pseudo-insects. This book covers only those orders that occur in New Zealand, and excludes those like the Zoraptera, Grylloblattodea and Embioptera that have never been found here. It also does not include species accounts for those orders whose members occur here but are small and relatively insignificant. These orders include the Psocoptera (book lice), Phthiraptera (parasitic lice), Thysanoptera (thrips) and Siphonaptera (fleas).

The insect orders represented in New Zealand are listed in the table on the next page; alongside each order and its literal meaning is an estimate of the total number of species so far recognised worldwide, as well as the number of species present in New Zealand and a local representative of the order. These figures, particularly in such cases as the Lepidoptera and Diptera, are very conservative. Ongoing taxonomic work continues to discover new species.

Insects in New Zealand

To fully understand the evolution of New Zealand's insects, a very short lesson in geology is necessary. Once arising as a series of volcanoes on the south-eastern edge of the giant continent of Gondwanaland, New Zealand first began its separation, and started on its 'drift' away, from Australia about 105 million years ago. The movement, brought about by the process of seafloor spreading, was slow at first, but the breakaway land mass really started moving between 60 and 80 million years ago. At even only a few centimetres a year you can go an awfully long way in 80 million years.

Order	Meaning	No. of species (NZ)	NZ examples
Thysanura	bristle tail	370 (5)	silverfish
Ephemeroptera	living for a day	2500 (40)	mayfly
Odonata	toothed (mandibles) flies	5000 (17)	dragonfly
Blattodea	avoiding light	4000 (30)	cockroach
Isoptera	equal wings	2300 (7)	termite
Mantodea	prophet-like	2000 (2)	mantis
Dermaptera	skin wings	1900 (20)	earwig
Plecoptera	wicker wings	3000 (100)	stonefly
Orthoptera	straight wings	20,000 (150)	weta
Psocoptera	milled wings	3000 (50)	book louse
Phthiraptera	louse, no wings	5000 (350)	parasitic louse
Phasmatodea	ghost-like	2500 (16)	stick insect
Hemiptera	half wings	82,000 (800)	cicada
Thysanoptera	fringed wings	5000 (35)	thrips
Megaloptera	large wings	300 (1)	dobsonfly
Neuroptera	nerve wings	5000 (16)	lacewing
Coleoptera	shield wings	400,000 (5500)	beetle
Mecoptera	long wings	500 (1)	scorpionfly
Siphonaptera	wingless tube	2500 (35)	flea
Diptera	two wings	125,000 (2000)	true fly
Trichoptera	hairy wings	8000 (200)	caddisfly
Lepidoptera	scaly wings	150,000 (2700)	butterfly
Hymenoptera	married (joined) wings	200,000 (600)	bees

Among the cargo on this voyage were the ancestors of many of the reptiles, birds and insects that we have here today. It appears likely that New Zealand did have mammals (as recent fossil discoveries have suggested), and one school of thought suggests they became extinct later, perhaps during the Oligocene period. The lack of mammals was to have a huge bearing on the evolution of our insect fauna.

With no rodents to prey on them, and few really efficient avian predators, insects here were able to evolve into many flightless and slow-moving forms, a classic example being that provided by the weta. Despite a fairly widely held misconception, weta are found in quite a few other countries besides New Zealand. Weta here, however, in the relatively benign environment prevailing in proto-Aotearoa, evolved into a number of interesting forms – in some cases filling the role of scavengers provided by mammals such as mice and rats elsewhere.

We could also claim, with some authority, to be the weevil capital of the world, in the sense that we are home to big, spectacular species like the speargrass weevils and some of the large, flightless weevils now confined to our offshore islands. There are around 50,000 weevils so far known worldwide, and we have about 1500 of them in New Zealand, including the world's longest, the giraffe weevil (*Lasiorhynchus barbicornis*), and smallest (*Myrtonymus zealandicus*), a small, blind species with no common name, which lives among the roots of trees like pohutukawa, kanuka and manuka.

Besides weevils and weta, we have several insects just as fascinating. The bat-winged fly (*Exsul singularis*), a creature of great beauty, and the wingless bat fly (*Mystacinobia zelandica*), a blind species that lives in intimate association with our native bats, are both of great interest to entomologists.

Flightlessness is undoubtedly the most noticeable characteristic of our insects, with a greater proportion of earth-bound insects, and a larger number of flightless representatives from these families, found in New Zealand than anywhere else on earth. Among insects that are normally fully winged there are flightless endemic New Zealand species of Plecoptera (stoneflies), most species of Blattodea (cockroaches), all Dermaptera (earwigs), Orthoptera (weta and grasshoppers), Phasmatodea (stick insects), Coleoptera (beetles), Diptera (flies) and Hymenoptera (ants, bees, wasps).

Flightlessness has other consequences. Geological events such as ice ages and orogenies (mountain building) often wiped out vast numbers of animals, with survivors clinging on in a few benign pockets called refugia. These isolated populations then quite often evolved into distinct species, sometimes with a very small geographic distribution.

A lack of wings proved to have serious and often fatal consequences when mammals were introduced by human agency: the kiore, or Polynesian rat, by Maori, and other rodents and mustelids by Europeans. Flightless insects were easy targets for these very efficient predators. We will probably never know just how many insect species have become extinct because of these introductions, but it is safe to assume that the number must run into the thousands.

From the initial period of separation of New Zealand, continuing to the present, the original voyagers have been joined here, at various times, by insects that have arrived by means of what geographers call the 'West Wind Drift'. This process continues to this day with, most noticeably, butterflies like the painted lady (*Cynthia kershawi*) and the lesser wanderer (*Danaus chrysippus petilia*) arriving in late spring on the prevailing westerlies.

Other recent arrivals, which could probably be called 'assisted immigrants' as they reached New Zealand as stowaways in cargo, are of much more concern because of the threats they pose both to humans and to our environment. These are species like the southern saltmarsh mosquito (*Ochlerotatus notoscriptus*), which can carry Ross River fever; various ant species, most notably the crazy ant (*Paratrechina longicornis*, not established yet and with eradication attempts underway), the Argentine ant (*Linepithema humile*, well and truly established) and the red fire ant (*Solenopsis invicta*, established temporarily but now eradicated), which are a grave threat to our native insects; and the gypsy moth (*Lymantria dispar*) and painted apple moth (*Teia anartoides*), both now eradicated, which can seriously damage trees.

Some of these species have been intercepted at borders and others have established temporarily but have been eradicated. However, there are many, such as the German and common wasps, which are among the approximately 2000 non-New Zealand insects that are now established in New Zealand.

The insect body

Put simply, an insect has a three-part body comprising a head, a thorax and an abdomen, with a pair of antennae and three pairs of legs. As with other arthropods the soft internal parts of the body are generally encased within a hard, chitinous exoskeleton, which is made up of separate plates and joined together by softer, pliable tissue so as to facilitate movement. This exoskeleton in some ways resembles a suit of armour and serves much the same purpose. Insects are the only invertebrates to have evolved wings, although it should be noted that this characteristic has been secondarily lost in many groups, particularly in New Zealand.

Since all these components and characteristics are infinitely variable, each is examined individually below.

Head

Insect heads are made up of six segments, which are fused together and which carry the eyes, mouth and antennae.

Most insects possess a pair of compound **eyes**, each of which is made up of a number of hexagonal facets called *ommatidia*. The ommatidia can be as few as two or three per eye, or even absent altogether, in the case of cave-dwelling species and insects like termites, or can number in the thousands, such as those found in dragonflies, which depend on good eyesight and distance judgement when hunting. Many insects also have three *ocelli* or simple eyes, situated between the compound eyes, which act as light receptors. These are quite obvious in insects such as cicadas.

The **mouth** is typically composed of an upper lip or *labrum*; jaw-like *mandibles*, which can be used for chewing or crushing and which can be enormous in species such as some of our stag beetles; *maxillae*, which lie behind the mandibles and are generally used for holding and manipulating food; and finally the *labium* or lower lip. The size and shape of the mouthparts can be extremely variable from one species to the next. In species like butterflies and moths, the mandibles have disappeared and been replaced by a tube-like device for sucking up liquids. This is the *proboscis*, and it is usually stored in a coiled position. In the true flies the mouthparts are fused together into suction-like pads so as to mop up liquids; and in mosquitoes they have been modified into a rigid proboscis used as a stabbing or piercing device.

The **antennae** are major sensory organs used for both touch and smell. They can be very variable, but are made up of three regions. The basal segment, that is, the part attached to the head, is called the *scape*. Next comes the *pedicel*, which is normally quite small, and the remaining segments are collectively called the *flagellum*.

Butterfly antennae   *Moth antennae*

Thorax

The thorax is basically a muscle-filled box to which the wings (where present) and legs are attached. It comprises three segments which, from front to back, are the *prothorax*, the *mesothorax* and the *metathorax*. Each thoracic segment carries a pair of legs, which again in front-to-back order are the anterior, the middle and the posterior pairs. In insects with two pairs of wings, the forewings are attached to the mesothorax and the posterior pair to the metathorax. In those with a single pair, such as the true flies (Diptera), these are borne on the mesothorax and the posterior wings are replaced by small club-shaped organs called *halteres*. These function as something akin to oscillating gyroscopes to help the fly maintain balance in flight.

Since the **legs** can be a useful tool in identifying some insects, the parts are listed here. Attached to the thorax is the basal or proximal joint, the *coxa*. Next comes the tiny *trochanter*; and then the *femur*, which in some of our orthopteran species can be greatly enlarged so as to facilitate jumping, and the tibia, which can sometimes be very long; and finally the distal region, the *tarsus*, usually composed of five segments, which often sports a pair of *tarsal claws*. Incidentally, most insects are deaf, the exceptions being species such as the cicadas, which use the tympanum in the abdomen for hearing as well as for making sound. In the Orthoptera, such as grasshoppers, 'ears' are situated on the forelegs.

Wings, too, are adapted to suit the individual requirements of the insect bearing them. The earliest insects had two pairs of wings, and these have evolved into the multiplicity of varieties seen today. There are, however, three basic types:

- Membranous wings in which the *venation* is clearly visible, e.g. dragonflies (Odonata). In some cases, such as the butterflies and moths (Lepidoptera), these are covered in scales.
- Toughened forewings that can be used in flight, as in the case of the grasshoppers (Orthoptera). These forewings are called *tegmina*.
- Hardened wing covers, called *elytra* (singular = *elytron*), which cannot be used in flight but which protect the hind wings and soft body parts, e.g. beetles.

Abdomen

The largest and softest part of the insect, the abdomen comprises up to 11 segments. It is used for the storage of fat and contains

9

the bulk of the digestive and excretory systems. It contains the *spiracles*, the holes or openings to the respiratory system. Air moves through an elaborate branching system of small tubes called *trachea*. Depending on the species, there may be other organs such as the *ovipositor* (egg-laying organ), the *stinger* (a modified ovipositor) and the *genitalia*. Some insects, in particular earwigs, carry a pair of large, forceps-like appendages on the last segment of the abdomen called *cerci*, used for defence and for crushing prey. In most other insects the cerci are sensory and may function as 'posterior antennae' (for example, in cockroaches they are sensitive to air movement and may warn of the approach of danger from behind), but mostly they are used in mating.

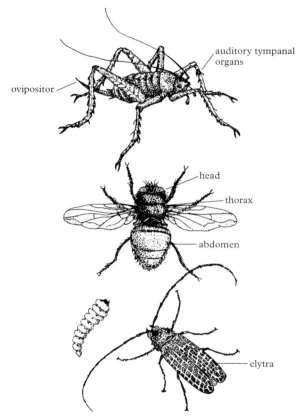

Variations on the three-part insect body comprising head, thorax and abdomen, with a pair of antennae and three pairs of legs. From top: Mahoenui giant weta, Deinacrida mahoenui, *native bluebottle,* Calliphora quadrimaculata, *huhu beetle and larva,* Prionoplus reticularis.

How to use this book

The entries in this book are arranged in established taxonomic order, as shown in the table on page 6, beginning with the most primitive orders, which are the silverfish (Thysanura), and finishing with the most advanced insects, which are the ants, bees and wasps (all Hymenoptera).

The list of orders can be divided into three main sections following this taxonomic grading.

The first (Thysanura only) are the most ancient, *ametabolous* insects, in which a nymph hatches from the egg as a miniature version of the adult. The nymph periodically moults its hard exoskeleton, each time exposing a fresh exoskeleton, which is slightly larger than the old one and soft at first and thus allows the nymph to grow before hardening off. Progressing through a series of such moults the nymph gets larger until it reaches full size and sexual maturity at the adult stage.

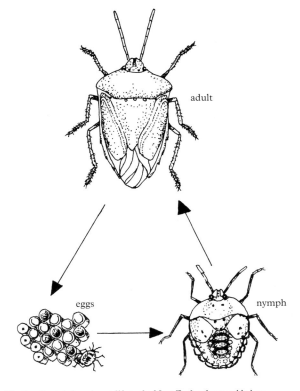

The hemimetabolous insect life cycle: New Zealand vegetable bug, Glaucias amyoti.

The second group (Ephemeroptera – Thysanoptera) are the *hemimetabolous* insects where the nymph becomes gradually more like the adult with each successive moult until the fully formed adult with complete wings and mature reproductive system emerges from the final moult. The number of nymph stages (instars) depends on the insect but is usually fixed for each species.

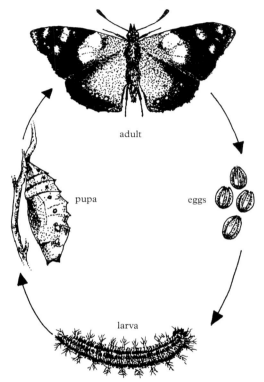

adult

pupa

eggs

larva

The holometabolous insect life cycle: yellow admiral, Bassaris itea.

The third portion (Megaloptera – Hymenoptera) of the list includes the *holometabolous* insects, which go through four stages: egg, larva, pupa and finally the adult that hatches from the pupa. Each stage is quite dissimilar to that succeeding it. The larvae of flying adults, for example, are frequently confined to a quite different habitat from that occupied by the adult, such as fresh water, rotten timber or soil.

There has been a tendency in a number of recent books to start with the butterflies and moths. The only reason for doing this is for aesthetics, as these are the most attractive and popular insects, and there is no scientific grounding behind this practice.

The coloured tabs on the side of each page give the order to which the insects belong. For each insect within the order, the common name is given first, followed by the scientific name and the average size of the insect featured. The first line of the main text gives the family to which it belongs, followed by the Maori name, should the insect have one. It should be noted that the size is the measurement from the front of the head to the tip of the abdomen in the adult. The exception is in the butterflies and moths, which are measured from wingtip to wingtip. The scientific names are those in current use, although more recent research may see some names superseded.

Thysanura: silverfish

Thysanura are among the most primitive of insects and are probably very similar in appearance to the very earliest insects to appear on earth. Some can make their own enzyme, cellulase, in the midgut, which allows them to digest cellulose. Very few insects can do this: only Thysanura, and some beetles. The rest rely on symbiotic bacteria in the gut to digest cellulose. Among the Thysanura, silverfish are a very ancient group of insects and have been around for some 300 million years.

Silverfish *Lepisma saccharina* 10 mm

Family Lepismatidae. The cosmopolitan silverfish arrived in New Zealand with the early European settlers and is now widespread throughout the country. The wingless silverfish adult is covered with silver-grey, glistening scales, hence the name. Here it is common in most houses and often chews starchy objects like paper, books and wallpaper, which it can digest (see introduction above). The female lays one to three eggs per day in sheltered places or may leave them exposed. The young instars are white at first and closely resemble the adult. The silverfish likes to hide during the day, preferring cracks and crevices. It will roam some distance for food, eating protein scraps and dead insects, including dead or injured of its own kind. However, it can also survive weeks without food or water.

Ephemeroptera: mayflies

The mayflies are considered by entomologists to be the most ancient and primitive of all winged insect orders, and first appeared in the Pre-Cambrian, 300 million years ago. Mayflies are easily distinguished from other aquatic insects by their transparent wings and their three long tail filaments. They are unique among insects for moulting again after reaching the fully adult winged stage, changing within a few hours from the rather dull 'dun' stage into shiny imagos or 'spinners'. In the northern hemisphere, mayflies first appear in May, so this is where the name originates. There are about 40 species in New Zealand. The winged adults have a short, or ephemeral, lifespan of one or two days, which they spend in the shelter of vegetation along stream-banks and lakeshores. Mating takes place over the water at dawn and dusk, after which the female lays her eggs in the water and then dies. The aquatic larvae, or nymphs, are flattened and have well-developed legs, enabling them to cling to rocks and stones in streams. The larvae grow in a series of moults, then crawl out of the water. When resting, all mayflies hold their wings vertically and sit with the abdomen pointed upwards.

Striped mayfly *Ameletopsis perscitus* 12 mm

Family Ameletopsidae. **Maori** piri wai. The striped mayfly is widespread throughout mainland New Zealand, with a preference for non-polluted waters. It is unique among our mayflies in having large, predatory, insectivorous nymphs, and the striped mayfly is one of the very few mayflies found anywhere in the world to have this characteristic. Although it prefers to lie in wait for its prey to swim by, it is capable of swimming if necessary to avoid predators. It is the only species in this genus found here, but other members of this family, also insectivorous, are found in Australia and South America.

Sucker-gilled mayfly *Deleatidium myzobranchia* 10 mm

Family Leptophlebiidae. **Maori** piri wai. The sucker-gilled mayfly is among the most prolific of our mayflies and is found in a wide range of habitats. It is particularly prevalent in fast-flowing rivers such as the stony braided rivers of Canterbury, where the flattened

body of the nymph enables it to cope easily with the strong currents. Here it is the most common insect and is an important food item for both native and introduced fish. The sucker-gilled mayfly is also preyed upon by wading birds, and in the higher reaches of streams and rivers it is an important component of the diet of the rare native blue duck (whio). Anglers call this species the pheasant tail brown dun. Related species like *Deleatidium autumnale* and *D. vernale* are also widespread.

Maui's mayfly *Mauiulus luma* 10 mm

Family Leptophlebiidae. **Maori** piri wai. Scattered populations of Maui's mayfly occur throughout the North Island, and with its close relative *Mauiulus aquilis*, it is an important food source for the blue duck (whio) in the higher reaches of streams and rivers. This is a native genus but not much is yet known about its biology. Although the *Mauiulus* genus is endemic, the Leptophlebiidae family is widespread throughout the world and the majority of Australasian mayflies belong to this group.

Double-gilled mayfly *Zephlebia nebulosa* 12 mm

Family Leptophlebiidae. **Maori** piri wai. More tolerant of still waters than other mayflies, the double-gilled mayfly is one of the more common species in the North Island, where the attractively patterned nymphs can often be seen on stones and logs along the shaded areas of streams. *Zephlebia cruentata*, which closely resembles *Z. nebulosa*, is also very common in the North Island. The nymphs of the *Zephlebia* genus have particularly long cerci and this is a useful diagnostic feature. Double-gilled mayflies are vegetarian, grazing on algae growing on submerged stones and logs.

Odonata: dragonflies and damselflies

New Zealand has 11 species of dragonflies and six of damselflies. Dragonflies and damselflies are a very ancient order of winged insects and have been around for some 250 million years. Normally, damselflies are smaller than dragonflies and hold their wings close to their bodies when resting, rather than holding them outstretched as dragonflies do. All the New Zealand species of dragonflies and damselflies are carnivorous, catching their prey, which includes caddisflies, crane flies, moths and aphids, while on the wing. Larvae, like adults, feed on animals smaller than themselves. Dragonflies have a unique method of copulation: the male and female grasp each other to form a 'copulation wheel' (see photo page 20). The females lay their eggs in water, on water plants, or in swampy ground. The larvae are sluggish with well-developed legs and compound eyes. They lack gills, so breathe by pumping air out of their rectums. At the end of larval growth, they crawl out of the water and undergo their final moults into adults. Adults have large eyes and antennae that are reduced to short bristles. The thorax is robustly built, and set at an angle so that the wings are inclined back and the legs gathered forward to form a 'basket' in which to trap prey. The abdomen is long and slender, and the wings are transparent with net-like veins.

A freshly emerged adult blue damselfly, Austrolestes colensonis, *drying its wings.*

Blue damselfly *Austrolestes colensonis* 45 mm

Blue damselfly, male.

Blue damselfly, female.

Family Lestidae. **Maori** kekewai. New Zealand's largest damselfly, this species is common along any stretch of still water throughout the three main islands, where it can often be seen from October to about May resting on vegetation edging the water. Although the females tend to be green, the males are bright blue, with their colouring becoming darker as colder weather approaches. The blue damselfly adult preys on smaller insects such as crane flies and true flies and in turn is often eaten by dragonflies and wasps. The nymph has an aquatic stage during which it feeds on minute crustaceans and fly larvae.

19

Redcoat damselfly *Xanthocnemis zealandica* 32 mm

Redcoat damselfly, male.

Recoat damselfly, female.

Redcoat damselflies in 'copulation wheel'.

Family Coenagrionidae. **Maori** kihitara. The most widespread of our damselflies, the native redcoat damselfly can be found just about anywhere, from brackish pools to alpine tarns throughout mainland New Zealand. The larvae also can be found in this wide variety of habitats. Eggs are deposited in slits that the female cuts in plants and the carnivorous larva is generally slow-moving, progressing forward by side-to-side undulations. The redcoat damselfly has been in New Zealand long enough to evolve into a number of related species, such as the Chatham redcoat damselfly, *Xanthocnemis tuanuii*, the alpine redcoat damselfly, *X. sinclairii*, and the kauri redcoat damselfly, *X. sobrina*. Overseas members of this group are called narrow-winged damselflies.

Red percher dragonfly *Diplacodes bipunctata* 32 mm

Red percher dragonfly, male.

Red percher dragonfly, female.

Family Libellulidae. **Maori** tiemiemi. The red percher dragonfly is a widespread species that, besides New Zealand, occurs also in Australia and in a number of islands in the south-east Pacific. Here, it is most common in Northland, but occasional specimens have been found as far south as Fiordland. It is distinguished from all the other New Zealand dragonflies by its reddish colour and small size. In summer the adult can often be observed sitting on rocks and banks or other flat surfaces near water. It has a habit of perching with its wings extended and held well forwards (see, especially, the lower photo). The species favours warm, shallow water, slowly flowing streams and weed-choked ponds. It will fly erratically if disturbed. Libellulidae is the most diverse and widespread of all dragonfly families. Overseas members of this group are known as common skimmers.

Sentry dragonfly *Hemicordulia australiae* 42 mm

Family Corduliidae. **Maori** tiemiemi. The medium-sized sentry dragonfly first arrived in New Zealand, probably from Australia, early in the 20th century, but became established only in the 1920s. It has colonised many parts of the North Island, and around Auckland it is now the commonest dragonfly. In the South Island it is very common. The male has brilliant metallic green eyes but the female's eyes are brown. The male hovers for long periods over its territory, hence the name 'sentry'. The female lays her eggs in vegetation edging on still water, such as that in swamps and ponds. The larva, which has a broad abdomen, takes two years to develop in the north, but longer in the colder southern areas.

Yellow-spotted dragonfly *Procordulia grayi* 50 mm

Family Corduliidae. **Maori** tiemiemi. The relatively large yellow-spotted dragonfly is a native species that occurs in many areas from south of the Waikato to Southland. However, it appears to have been driven out of a number of its traditional haunts by the sentry dragonfly (see previous entry). The adult's thorax is green and the abdomen is brownish with two longitudinal rows of large yellow-orange spots clearly visible when the species is in flight. It is a powerful, swift flier, keeping close to the ground. Breeding typically occurs in still waters such as that provided by lakes, ponds and tarns, but individuals have been seen hunting over scrubland some distance from water. The larval development is believed to take about two years. The ranger dragonfly (*Procordulia smithi*) is similar to this species, but is more greenish in colour. *P. smithi* is also more widely distributed, even reaching the Chatham Islands.

Bush giant dragonfly *Uropetala carovei* 82 mm

Family Petaluridae. **Maori** kakapowai. This large dragonfly, with its distinctive black and yellowish abdomen, is widespread throughout the North Island, but in the South Island appears restricted to northern and western areas. It favours rough forest land and scrub country. A slow and noisy flier, it is a voracious hunter and takes its prey on the wing. Prey includes flies, cicadas, wasps and butterflies. The adult sometimes perches and basks for long periods on the outer vegetation or trunks of trees. The female lays her eggs along the muddy margins of streams and ponds or where there is a lot of groundwater seepage. Here the larva constructs a long tunnel in mud, clay or peat, which it lives in for about six years before emerging as an adult. This dragonfly is also known as the devil's darning needle.

Mountain giant dragonfly *Uropetala chiltoni* 80 mm

Family Petaluridae. **Maori** kakapowai. This very large, yellow-and-black dragonfly is very similar to the bush giant dragonfly (see previous entry), only slightly larger, but this species differs in having a yellow patch on its upper lip, or labrum. It is not known from the North Island but lives in parts of Canterbury and Otago where the bush giant dragonfly is absent, frequenting streams and tarns in upland areas. A slow and noisy flier, it can be seen over scrub or tussock. The adult often perches and basks for long periods on rocks. The female lays her eggs in hillside seepages containing tussock.

23

Blattodea: cockroaches

If a vote was taken to name the world's most unpopular insect, the cockroach would win hands down. This is a pity, as only 1–2 per cent of the estimated 4000 species are pests. Most cockroaches are clean-living, non-aggressive species, living chiefly in tropical rainforests. Some are attractively patterned, and in Europe and North America they are often kept as pets. For the record, the largest cockroach may be the Australian species, *Macropanesthia rhinocerus*, which weighs in at 50 grams. Imagine finding one of those under your fridge!

In New Zealand there are some 25 species of native cockroaches from five genera, all of which are fairly similar. Unlike the introduced species, they are generally flightless. Some are confined to the scree slopes of the South Island, but others are widespread. Generally, they are brown or black, with the exception of the attractive orange, high-country species, the alpine cockroach (*Celatoblatta quinquemaculata*). There is also a bicoloured species, *Maoriblatta rufoterminata*, which is confined to kauri forests of Northland and the Coromandel Peninsula.

Bush cockroach *Celatoblatta vulgaris* 12 mm

The bush cockroach is being attacked by the black cockroach hunter, Tachysphex nigerrimus *(see page 133). The female wasp hunts and paralyses cockroach nymphs and brings them back to her sandy burrow to feed to her larvae.*

Family Blatellidae. **Maori** kekerengu. Unlike the introduced cockroaches, the native bush cockroach is not normally found indoors, but is sometimes inadvertently brought into the house on material like firewood. The female lays eggs in egg cases (with several eggs per case) usually under the loose bark of trees, and you can often find egg cases when you peel layers of bark on trees such as manuka and kanuka. The bush cockroach is omnivorous, eating just about anything, and is even able to digest dead wood with the help of its symbiotic gut flora.

Gisborne cockroach *Drymaplaneta semivitta* 25 mm

Family Blatellidae. The name Gisborne cockroach is a misnomer, as this species first appeared in New Zealand in 1954 in Tauranga, probably arriving here in a log shipment. From Tauranga it has now spread over most of the North Island, and is also reported from Nelson. As in its native West Australia, this species is primarily an outdoor creature, but in New Zealand it may venture indoors. The other species normally encountered indoors are the German cockroach (*Blatella germanica*), a smaller (12 mm), drab brown insect with conspicuous wings; and in the Auckland area, the larger American cockroach (*Periplaneta americana*, 40 mm). Being a tropical species, this last cockroach tends to prefer warmer areas, such as that afforded by hospitals and bakeries. The American and German species live up to the public's perception of these pests. Besides spoiling food with their excrement, they further contaminate food with a liquid they discharge from their mouths in order to soften whatever they are eating. They also spread bacteria. Cockroaches live communally but without the organisational structure of social insects such as bees and ants.

Isoptera: termites

In some countries such as Australia termites build large, distinctive mounds, sometimes called anthills and sometimes temitariums, which are hard to miss as they can be up to several metres in height. Termites in New Zealand, however, are small, inconspicuous creatures that generally go unnoticed until part of your house collapses. They are very social insects living in large, multi-caste societies with a reigning king and queen, along with subordinate soldiers and workers. Although often referred to as 'white ants', the termites are not related to the ants.

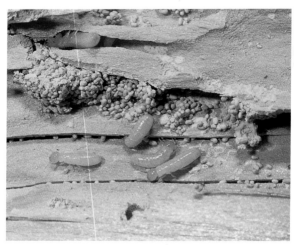

New Zealand drywood termites in timber.

Tunnels of drywood termites.

New Zealand drywood termite *Kalotermes brouni* 4 mm

New Zealand drywood termite, winged adults.

Cuni de Graaf

Termite adult.

Family Kalotermitidae. **Maori** popokorua ma. The New Zealand drywood termite is one of three native species of termites and it is widely distributed throughout New Zealand north of about Christchurch. Termites are divided into three groups – drywood, dampwood and subterranean – and this species, as its name indicates, belongs to the drywood group. The New Zealand drywood termite is found in stumps, rotten logs, fence posts and other timber, but it does occasionally invade living trees through damaged areas. The adult termite has a brief winged period when leaving its home colony to establish new ones. A related species, *Kalotermes banksiae*, has recently become established in New Zealand.

27

Mantodea: mantises

Although there are about 2000 mantises worldwide, in New Zealand there are only two, one native and one introduced. They are very distinctive insects, which can easily be spotted as they wait for their prey with their forelegs raised as if in prayer, poised to snatch any unsuspecting insect. Their scientific name of Mantodea comes from the Greek word for prophet. At night they quite often gather around lights and seize the insects that these lights attract. The names used by the Maori for mantises, whe and ro, are also used for stick insects.

Springbok mantis mating (see entry below).

Springbok mantis *Miomantis caffra* 40 mm

Springbok mantis laying eggs.

Family Mantidae. **Maori** whe. Although this mantis only arrived in New Zealand from its native South Africa sometime in the 1970s, it has now supplanted the native mantis, *Orthodera novaezealandiae* (see next entry), over much of the northern part of the North Island. The large, conspicuous egg case, called an ootheca, can often be found on the more sheltered parts of fences and buildings. Unlike the native mantis, which is green, the springbok mantis ranges from pink to beige and can also be green. The adult feeds on a wide range of insects from flies to cicadas. The female shares the charming habit of other mantises of eating her mate during and after mating.

New Zealand praying mantis *Orthodera novaezealandiae* 40 mm

Young mantises emerging from case.   *Female making egg case.*

Family Mantidae. **Maori** whe. Our sole native mantis is green. It has a further distinguishing mark – a purple or blue dot on its forelegs, a feature that is absent in the springbok mantis. Although winged, the New Zealand praying mantis seldom flies, preferring to stalk its victims, and is so efficient a predator that it can capture up to 25 flies a day, causing some people to suggest a more apt name might be 'preying mantis'. The female constructs an ootheca, with a double row of white chambers, which is much neater than that of the springbok mantis, and in this she deposits several hundred eggs. The young, when they emerge from the egg case, are mini-ature versions of the adult, moulting at intervals and taking about a year to reach their full size.

29

Dermaptera: earwigs

DERMAPTERA

Earwigs get their common name from the fancied resemblance of their hardened forewings or tegmina to a human ear. There was also an erroneous belief held in Europe in the Middle Ages that earwigs crawled into the ears of sleeping people, then drilled into their brains, thereby killing the person. Due to their fondness for living in pot plants, earwigs are often encountered by home gardeners.

In New Zealand, as well as the seashore earwig (*Anisolabis littorea*; see entry below) there are other species of native earwigs, including a number which live in alpine areas, mostly *Parisolabis* species such as *P. novaezealandicus* and *P. tapanuiensis*.

Seashore earwig *Anisolabis littorea* 30 mm

Family Labiduridae. **Maori** mata. The Maori name for this native species, mata, meaning obsidian, refers to its dark colour. The seashore earwig seldom occurs far from the coast and can be found under suitable bits of seaweed and driftwood on most beaches in the North Island, and in the South Island to as far south as Dunedin in the east and Jackson Bay in the west. Here it ekes out an existence preying on small invertebrates such as sandhoppers, attacking these at speed, curling its abdomen over the back and crushing its victims with its strong pincers. It also eats seaweed. The mother is a devoted guardian, cleaning the eggs of fungus with her mandibles and looking after the young once they hatch until they are big enough to fend for themselves. However, if times get tough, she is not above eating her own eggs.

European earwig *Forficula auricularia* 15 mm

Family Forficulidae. **Maori** hiore kakati. Accidentally introduced into New Zealand by early European settlers, this species is now well established. Although it eats almost anything, it is particularly partial to stone-fruit such as peaches, nectarines and apricots, and so is the bane of orchardists. Although it is capable of burrowing, the European earwig commonly lurks under logs and stones, from where it emerges at night to feed on detritus and dead organic matter. It also feeds on live plant tissue, particularly flower petals. The Maori name means 'grasping tail', which is a reference to this animal's very pronounced cerci. Like the seashore earwig (see previous entry), the adult female of this species is a devoted mother, carefully tending her young. This care has its limits, however, as once adult the young are quite likely to eat their mother, or vice versa. Although winged, the European earwig seldom flies. The recently arrived Australian earwig (*Labidura truncata*) is rather similar, but has a much longer pair of cerci in proportion to its body.

Plecoptera: stoneflies

New Zealand has over 100 species of stoneflies and all are native. Adult stoneflies are weak fliers, and usually live in the vicinity of the streams which support their larvae. They can often be found on the overhanging vegetation, or on rocks, along stream-banks. The larvae (nymphs) tend to prefer areas of water movement. They have long bodies and long jointed antennae, and some have small, paired abdominal gills. Stoneflies in New Zealand are interesting, as the alpine populations of some species are wingless, and in other species, the lowland forms have wings; the large green stonefly (*Stenoperla prasina*, see page 33) provides a good example of this phenomenon.

Black stonefly *Austroperla cyrene* 16 mm

Black stoneflies mating.

Family Austroperlidae. The black stonefly is widely distributed throughout the three main islands of New Zealand from sea level to around 1600 m. Although it can be found in a wide variety of aquatic habitats, it prefers flowing water in which to deposit its eggs. Here the nymph lives on decaying vegetation, unlike the nymph of the large green stonefly, which is insectivorous. Also unlike the larvae of other stonefly species, which are cryptically coloured, the black stonefly nymph is distinctively patterned in white, black and yellow. This serves to warn predators that the insect is distasteful, and tests have shown it has a high concentration of hydrogen cyanide in its body.

Large green stonefly *Stenoperla prasina* 30 mm

Family Eustheniidae. **Maori** ngarongaro wai. This species is one of our largest stoneflies and the deepest green in colour. It occurs widely throughout mainland New Zealand, from lowland streams to alpine lakes and tarns. However, it seeks out faster-flowing water in which to deposit its eggs, the female laying between 100 and 1000 eggs. These can take up to a year to hatch, and the developing nymph preys on the larvae of other insects, particularly those of the mayflies and midges. The large green stonefly nymph in turn is sought out by wading birds and blue duck (whio). The larval stage lasts from one to three years but the adult survives for only about a week. There are three other species in this genus, one of which, the upland stonefly (*Stenoperla helsoni*), is flightless.

Large green stonefly nymph.

Orthoptera: weta and grasshoppers

Orthoptera is a group of large and instantly recognisable insects, all of which have prominent hind legs designed for jumping, and a conspicuous pronotum (the dorsal surface of the prothorax, behind the head). Orthoptera are divided into two sub-orders, the Ensifera and the Caelifera. The ensiferans, the group that includes our weta, all have long antennae, which are at least half the length of the body and often much longer, and the females sport prominent ovipositors. The caeliferans, to which our alpine grasshoppers belong, have short antennae and no ovipositors. There are over 20,000 described orthopterans and New Zealand has around 150 known species, with probably at least that number still to be described.

Bluff weta *Deinacrida elegans* 50 mm

George Gibbs

Family Anostostomatidae. **Maori** weta. The native bluff weta was only named in 1999 and is found in a relatively restricted area, between Marlborough and Mt Somers in Canterbury, at altitudes of between 600 and 1725 m. By day it lives in rock crevices, emerging at night to graze on alpine vegetation such as *Helichrysum*, alpine daisies and buttercups. Like other giant weta, it probably also eats dead insects if the opportunity arises. If alarmed it drops off its perch and rolls down the slope.

Mahoenui giant weta *Deinacrida mahoenui* 100 mm

Family Anostostomatidae. **Maori** weta punga. The native Mahoenui giant weta has a very restricted range, so far having been found only in a patch of gorse at Mahoenui near Te Kuiti. Other species of giant weta are equally rare, and most are now restricted to offshore islands or mountain ranges. For example, *Deinacrida heteracantha* is known only from Little Barrier Island and *D. connectens* and *D. elegans* are both alpine species. Their biology is not well known, but presumably the female, using her ovipositor, lays her eggs in the ground. These weta live for up to about four years, and a fully grown female is likely to weigh 50 grams, making it one of the heaviest of all insects. Not all giant weta are so big; some are smaller than tree weta. In recent years Mahoenui giant weta have been translocated to a number of reserves such as the Cowan Wildlife Reserve (North Pureora Forest) and Warrenheip Reserve (near Cambridge), which exercise rigorous predator controls. A captive breeding programme for the species is now under way at Auckland Zoo.

Giant scree weta *Deinacrida pluvialis* 55 mm

John Early

Giant scree weta at Franz Josef Glacier, Westland, c. 1400 m.

Family Anostostomatidae. **Maori** weta. The giant scree weta is an alpine specialist, which lives along the western side of the main divide, from Mt Alexander in the Kaimata Range, to as far south as the Cleddau Cirque, which is in the Darran Mountains of Fiordland. Like other *Deinacrida* it is generally herbivorous, but will eat dead insects if they are available. Eggs are deposited throughout the year, but most hatching takes place during the summer. On the eastern side of the main divide, this species is replaced by the scree weta, *D. connectens*.

Mountain stone weta *Hemideina maori* 55 mm

John Early

Family Anostostomatidae. **Maori** weta. The native mountain stone weta is found at medium to high altitudes in the South Island, from Nelson to as far south as the Rock and Pillar Range in Otago. Although technically a tree weta, it often lives among schist and under scree, far above the tree line. It is a particularly interesting weta in that it is the largest insect that can survive being frozen solid for several days and emerge unscathed. This is an omnivorous species. Eggs are laid year round, but particularly in late autumn with the larvae hatching in the following summer.

Auckland tree weta *Hemideina thoracica* 65 mm

Auckland tree weta: male (top); female (bottom).

Family Anostostomatidae. **Maori** putangatanga. Although its common name suggests that this weta is found only around Auckland, it actually occurs over a much wider area – throughout the northern North Island, as far south as a line running between Mt Taranaki and northern Hawke's Bay. South of this line it is replaced by the Wellington tree weta (*Hemideina crassidens*), which is found as far south as Canterbury. This differs from the Auckland species in having a body covered with alternating black and yellow bands. Although it has a fearsome appearance, the tree weta is a relatively harmless vegetarian and scavenger, emerging at night to dine on leaves, flowers and fruit such as those of the lacebark and mahoe; it will eat dead insects too. The female (see lower photo) can lay eggs all year round, but April and May are the preferred months. It is then that the weta descends to the ground and lays up to 200 eggs in the soil. The young go through several moults, taking about a year to reach maturity. The auditory tympanal organs ('ears') of the tree and ground weta are situated on the creature's forelegs (see illustration, page 10).

Cave weta *Gymnoplectron longipes* 30 mm

Cave weta, G. longipes.

Cave weta, G. uncata.

Family Rhaphidophoridae. **Maori** weta. The native cave weta *Gymnoplectron longipes* is widely distributed throughout the North Island, but is replaced in the South Island by other species. The cave weta or tokoriro (*G. uncata*; 30 mm) is widely distributed in caves and forest in the central North Island. Although the body of cave weta species is relatively small (much smaller than tree weta; see previous entry), their limbs and antennae are proportionately very long (much longer than tree weta). In fact, they can extend to 45 cm from the antennae to the tips of the hind legs. Cave weta are generally vegetarian but also scavenge on dead invertebrates. For example, two species that live on the Chathams, *Talitropsis crassicruris* and *Novoplectron serratum*, are suspected of eating carrion (some may feed on the carcases of dead seabirds). Although known as cave weta, the New Zealand species live in a variety of domiciles as well as caves, including hollow logs, holes in tree trunks and even in water tanks. They also rapidly colonise tunnels and culverts. Some of New Zealand's cave weta are preyed upon by our largest spider, the Nelson cave spider (*Spelungula cavernicola*). They are also relished by kiwi. Cave weta are sometimes known as weta taipo or goblin weta. Auditory tympanal organs (see illustration, page 10) are absent in cave weta.

Migratory locust *Locusta migratoria* 50 mm

Family Acrididae. **Maori** kapakapa. The migratory locust is found throughout the North Island and as far south as Mid Canterbury. It frequents patches of low, uncultivated grasses and secondary growth, and can often be found in sand dunes. Overseas, it is very widespread, ranging from Australia through Asia to Africa. This is the only locust species to be found here and, despite its name, in New Zealand it never migrates. The female deposits her eggs in the ground in autumn. The young hatches in the spring as a smaller, wingless version of the adult, and it is only after several moults that it matures into a fully winged and developed adult. Locusts are entirely vegetarian.

Hairy alpine grasshopper *Brachaspis nivalis* 20 mm

Family Acrididae. **Maori** mawhitiwhiti. The native hairy alpine grasshopper is widespread at higher altitudes throughout mountainous areas of the South Island (600–1800 m), from the Black Birch Mountains of Marlborough to as far south as the Old Man Range and the Barrier Range, behind Twizel. It can often be located on alpine cushion and herbfields but prefers rocky areas such as scree slopes, high rocky ridges or the stony edges of streams, where

George Gibbs

its cryptic colouration (slate grey or a mottled grey) makes it hard to spot unless it moves. It is a herbivorous species and the duration of the larval period seems to be dependent on food availability. A diurnal species, it is sometimes also called the scree grasshopper. Males (15–24 mm) are smaller than females (16–40 mm).

39

Mackenzie Basin grasshopper *Sigaus minutus* 16 mm

Brian Patrick

Family Acrididae. **Maori** mawhitiwhiti. The native Mackenzie Basin grasshopper is one of New Zealand's smallest grasshoppers (adult males are 10–17 mm; females 15–20 mm) and certainly one of our rarest, having so far been located only in two small patches of scabweed (*Raoulia australis*) on river floodplain flats in the Mackenzie Country of Central Otago. It occurs in two colour variations (one dark, one pale), but its biology has been little studied. It is probably generally omnivorous, eating fresh foliage and dead insects when it can get them.

North Island grasshopper *Sigaus piliferus* 35 mm

Family Acrididae. **Maori** mawhitiwhiti. This grasshopper is widespread over much of the North Island, from the Coromandel Peninsula southwards, but is more common and generally a larger size in montane areas. It is a flightless, diurnal species that feeds on grasses and other foliage. Its preferred habitat is tussock grasslands. The North Island grasshopper is one of 26 native species of grasshoppers, belonging to the four endemic genera, *Alpinacris*, *Brachaspis*, *Paprides* and *Sigaus*. (There are also two species from the genus *Phaulacridium*; the species are endemic but the genus isn't – it also occurs in Australia.) Many endemic species are restricted in range to a single mountain or alpine valley, and several are protected.

New Zealand grasshopper *Phaulacridium marginale* 15 mm

New Zealand grasshoppers mating.

Family Acrididae. **Maori** mawhitiwhiti. The native New Zealand grasshopper is common throughout mainland New Zealand at low to mid altitudes on grassy flats, bush clearings, mine tailings and sand dunes. It is highly variable in colour, ranging from pink through brown to green, depending on the background in which it is found.

This is one of our two *Phaulacridium* species; the other is *P. otagoense*, which is found only in Central Otago and the Mackenzie Basin. The genus is also found in Australia and a very rare species, *P. howeanum*, is restricted to one tiny area on Mt Gower on Lord Howe Island.

New Zealand grasshopper, another colour variation.

41

Katydid *Caedicia simplex* 40 mm

Family Tettigoniidae. **Maori** kiki pounamu. The katydid is widespread throughout mainland New Zealand and is also common in Australia. It occurs widely in gardens and hedges, where it

feeds on vegetation, and spends considerable time grooming itself, but its cryptic colouration affords it very effective camouflage, so it is not easy to spot – except when it is feeding on the bronze-leaved manuka in gardens. The katydid nymphs (the final stage is pictured) are sometimes pink-red but adults are always green. Strollers in country areas on summer nights will hear the katydid's quiet, rather staccato 'zip-zip' song, which gives it one of its alternative names, the scissor snip.

Black field cricket *Teleogryllus commodus* 20 mm

Family Gryllidae. **Maori** pihareinga. The black field cricket is widespread throughout the North Island and it also occurs in warmer areas of the South Island. It is also found in Australia. In late summer and autumn, its whirring chirps are a familiar sound as it emerges in the evening from cracks in the soil, rock crevices and from under stones, particularly in uncultivated areas like roadside verges

and bush fringes. Only the adult male chirps, which it does by rubbing its wings together. It is entirely vegetarian and is not too discriminating in what it eats. After long dry periods it can reach plague proportions in grassy fields. The female lays her white, oblong eggs in the soil and the hatchling, a miniature version of the adult, takes about nine months to reach maturity. Although it can fly if harassed, the cricket prefers to run or jump.

Mole cricket *Triamescaptor aotea* 20 mm

ORTHOPTERA

George Gibbs

Family Gryllotalpidae. **Maori** honi. Once widespread throughout mainland New Zealand, the mole cricket has been collected at only a few localities in the south of the North Island and on D'Urville Island in recent years. It is wingless and nocturnal, with strongly developed forelegs. It digs circular galleries in the soil where it rears its young, and feeds on roots, grass grubs and larvae. Unlike mole crickets overseas, which are noted for their loud and distinctive songs, this native species is silent. Its scarcity nowadays may be due to predation by rats.

Phasmatodea: stick insects

These quite large insects are fairly common in wooded areas throughout New Zealand. All our stick insect species are flightless, relying on their superb camouflage for survival. Of course, this

feature also means you will not detect them easily. The name Phasmatodea means ghost-like, and presumably refers to their gait, as they walk slowly and often sway from side to side. Females lay their eggs in autumn and die off in the winter, with the young emerging the following spring. Overseas some stick insects, including New Zealand species, are kept as pets. In Australia, some species of stick insects can reach plague proportions, completely defoliating and thus killing trees. This phenomenon has never occurred here.

Rough-skinned stick insect, Acanthoxyla prasina suteri *(see entry opposite).*

Prickly stick insect *Acanthoxyla prasina prasina* 110 mm

Prickly stick insect, Acanthoxyla prasina prasina.

Family Phasmatidae. **Maori** wairaka. The native prickly stick insect is often called a 'walking stick'. It is widespread throughout New Zealand and browses the leaves of a number of tree species, but it is particularly partial to the foliage of the various *Metrosideros* species such as pohutukawa and the various rata trees and vines. It can also sometimes be found on rimu, totara and kahikatea. In trees, it lurks among the branches and is very effectively camouflaged. If discovered, it will often fall to the ground and 'play possum'. Most of this genus of stick insects are female, being the product of unfertilised eggs, a process called parthenogenesis. The downside is that the stick insects have an identical genetic make-up to their mothers and, because of this limited gene pool, are thus less able to cope with changing conditions. Like the common stick insect, the prickly stick insect was accidentally introduced into England, arriving there in a consignment of New Zealand plants in 1909.

Another form of *Acanthoxyla prasina* is the rough-skinned stick insect (*A. p. suteri*, also 100 mm; see photo opposite). It is probably the most widespread of our stick insects, being found throughout mainland New Zealand and on a number of near offshore islands such as Great Barrier.

Common stick insect *Clitarchus hookeri* 110 mm

Family Phasmatidae. **Maori** ro. The native common stick insect is found throughout mainland New Zealand and on a number of adjoining offshore islands. Both the male and female range in colour from green to brown, but the juvenile is often reddish-brown. In this

species the male is significantly smaller than the female, and the general belief is fertilised eggs result in males and females, whereas eggs produce only males. Look for this species among the leaves of kanuka, manuka and pohutukawa, which are its preferred food. *Clitarchus hookeri* is sometimes called the smooth stick insect. Like the prickly stick insect, the common stick insect was accidentally introduced into England, arriving there in a consignment of New Zealand plants in 1909.

Brown stick insect *Micrarchus hystriculeus* 90 mm

Family Phasmatidae. **Maori** ro. The genus *Micrarchus* is endemic to New Zealand, and this species is found throughout the South Island and in southern parts of the North Island. Unlike some of

our other stick insects, the male in this species is only slightly smaller than the female. Their colouration, like other stick insects, is somewhat variable, ranging from green to brown. Little seems to be known about the biology of this species, but it has been found on *Hymenanthera*, a small-leaved shrub, which is a rather unusual food for stick insects. The species was formerly known as *Pachymorpha hystriculea*.

46

Ridge-backed stick insect *Tectarchus diversus* 80 mm

Family Phasmatidae. **Maori** ro. The native ridge-backed stick insect is found throughout the two main islands. The male is only slightly smaller than the female, and the colour of both ranges from green to brown, with speckled examples being not uncommon. The ridge running along the back, which gives this stick insect its common name, is not as pronounced in the male, but is an obvious feature of the female.

Hemiptera: aphids, planthoppers, cicadas, true bugs

Although there is a tendency for many people to call all insects bugs, technically the true bugs are a sub-order of Hemiptera, all of which have modified mouthparts, called a rostrum, that enable them to pierce the skins of plants or animals and to suck up the sap or blood they use as food. They are divided into three sub-orders: the Auchenorrhyncha, which are the planthoppers and cicadas; the Sternorrhyncha, which includes groups like the aphids, mealybugs and scales; and the Heteroptera, or true bugs. Hemiptera is the most successful order of hemimetabolous insects and includes a multitude of varied and diverse insects. New Zealand has over 40 species of cicadas, and about 800 species of bugs, out of the approximately 82,000 species so far described worldwide.

Cicadas, which generally feed on tree sap, are known for their often strident call. Only the male cicada sings, to attract the female. It produces one of the loudest sounds in the insect world from a sound organ, the tympanum in the abdomen, that has a drum-like structure which is vibrated by strong muscles. Another noticeable feature of cicadas is the shed nymph skins (known as exuvia) that are seen on tree trunks. The female lays eggs in branches, and when the nymph hatches it drops to the ground and enters the soil, sucking sap from tree roots. Although cicadas overseas spend as many as 16 years underground before pupating, it appears those in New Zealand spend considerably less, possibly one to three years in most species. The nymph finally emerges from the soil, climbs a tree trunk and splits its skin down the back. The adult emerges, expands its wings and flies away.

Aphids, as sap-suckers, are serious pests of many plant species and are also known for being virus carriers. They are found on a range of native and introduced, indoor and outdoor plants, and are a significant pest in both kiwifruit and avocado orchards. They are to be found on the trunk, branches and foliage of their host plants. Fortunately many insects prey on aphids, including ladybirds, wasps and mantises and so help to control them.

Chorus cicada, Amphipsalta zealandica, male *(see entry opposite)*.

Chorus cicada *Amphipsalta zealandica* 26 mm

Chorus cicada female laying eggs (top), eggs (left), nymph (right).

Family Cicadidae. **Maori** kihikihi wawa. The native chorus cicada is one of the most widespread of New Zealand's cicadas and is the largest species. It is found throughout the North Island and in most of the South Island, apart from coastal Otago. It is also present on Stewart Island and the Three Kings Islands. The chorus cicada frequents tall trees, feeding on sap, and adults have a short season and die off over winter. Males call in unison 'te te te eeka', and the massed sound created is quite deafening and was likened by Maori to heavy rain, which they called wawa. This sound was important as it marked the start of the eighth month of the Maori calendar. The chorus cicada male also produces loud clicks as wings are clapped against tree trunks. As it generally sings from the tree canopies, it is not often seen. The female lays eggs in herringbone-patterned slots in branches, and when the nymph hatches out the following spring it drops to the ground and enters the soil, sucking sap from tree roots. After one to three years the nymph emerges from the soil, climbs a tree trunk and splits its skin down the back, whereupon the adult emerges, expands its wings and flies away. The nymph skins (exuvia) seen on tree trunks are a bright brown, compared with the pale brown ones of the other *Amphipsalta* species, *A. cingulata*.

April green cicada *Kikihia ochrina* 24 mm

April green cicada, K. ochrina.

Family Cicadidae. **Maori** kihikihi kai. The April green cicada is present in both the North Island and the top of the South, but is not so common in Northland. It usually occurs in the same areas as the little grass cicada, *Kikihia muta,* but the April green cicada's call is a constant and monotonous 'didididididi', while the little grass cicada's call is 'zee zit zit zit'. Both are particularly noisy from Christmas until about May, and a large congregation of cicadas in full voice can reach up to 100 decibels. A related cicada, with a similar call, lives on the Chatham Islands. This is the Chathams cicada, *K. longula.*

Little grass cicada, K. muta.

Snoring cicada *Kikihia cutora* 20 mm

Family Cicadidae. **Maori** kihikihi. The snoring cicada is found throughout the northern North Island, to as far south as National Park, in a wide variety of habitats ranging from coastal dunes up to the tops of mountains. It is also found on some of the offshore islands, reaching as far north as the Kermadec Islands. It can be heard in most seasons of the year. The song goes 'it it it it – dambo dambo dambo'. Maori likened the speech of Europeans to the calls of cicada, as to their ears it was fairly strident compared to their more mellifluous language.

High alpine cicada *Maoricicada nigra* 12 mm

High alpine cicada at Temple Basin, near Arthur's Pass.

George Gibbs

Family Cicadidae. **Maori** kihikihi. The high alpine cicada and the allied species *Maoricicada oromelaena* are considered to be some of the highest dwelling cicadas in the world. They live in the Southern Alps, from Nelson to as far south as Fiordland, at 1200 to 1850 m altitude. Here they frequent scree slopes, fellfields and herbfields, where the male's distinctive chattering call, 'er-chit-er-chit-er-chit', can be heard often in spring. Like those of all cicadas, the nymphs are herbivorous, spending several years underground feeding on the roots of a variety of plants.

Red-tailed cicada *Rhodopsalta cruentata* 16 mm

Family Cicadidae. **Maori** kihikihi. One of the prettiest cicadas, the red-tailed cicada is found throughout the North Island, and south to North Canterbury and northern Westland in the South Island. It is particularly common in sand dunes and along stream- and river-banks. It has a small, weak and somewhat monotonous call, which sounds something like 'tiktak tiktak tiktak', and this is produced by the male while it is sheltering among shrubbery. It is suspected that *Rhodopsalta* species spend three to six years underground before emerging to become adult. This species could be confused with *R. microdora*, which shares much of the same habitat, but *R. microdora* is more greenish in colouration.

Oleander aphid *Aphis nerii* 2 mm

Family Aphididae. **Maori** kutu riki. The cosmopolitan oleander aphid, distinctive with its yellow body and black appendages, is an introduced species, probably from Britain, that is now widespread throughout New Zealand. This species probably originated in the Mediterranean region, the origin of its principal host plant, the oleander. It can be found, often in great abundance, on the trunk, branches and foliage of its host plants, which are a range of native and introduced indoor and outdoor plants. On orchard crops such as kiwifruit and avocados, the sap-sucking aphid is a considerable pest. The adult female deposits nymphs rather than eggs and these are clones of the female. The nymph progresses through five instars.

Grey planthopper *Anzora unicolor* 8 mm

Family Flatidae. An Australian introduction, the grey planthopper is now widespread throughout mainland New Zealand. When resting, the wings are held above the body, giving this planthopper a triangular appearance. It is well camouflaged when resting among twigs and branches. The nymphs, just like those of the passion vine hopper (see page 54) and the green planthopper (see next entry), have a fluffy posterior and are sometimes called 'fluffy bums' by children. As the common name suggests, both adult and nymph tend to jump away when disturbed. Like others in its family, the nymph sucks the sap of plants, often damaging them. It is also suspected of being a vector of the viral disease affecting cabbage trees.

Green planthopper *Siphanta acuta* 12 mm

Family Flatidae. Like the grey planthopper (see previous entry) this species is an Australian introduction, now widespread throughout mainland New Zealand. It, too, raises its wings above its body, and when at rest, particularly on green branches, it resembles spines, which helps it avoid predation. Although most individuals are green, some blue and yellow specimens are seen. When disturbed, both adult and nymph tend to jump away, rather than fly. The female lays clusters of eggs on leaves, which hatch in the spring. It is of concern to orchardists because it transmits fire blight, a bacterial disease, to pip-fruit trees. The nymph also has a fluffy posterior phase.

Passion vine hopper *Scolypopa australis* 7 mm

Passion vine hopper adult and nymphs.

Family Ricaniidae. The passion vine hopper arrived here from Australia in the 1870s and is now well established from Nelson northwards. Although an abundant bug here, in its native Australia it is considered to be fairly rare. It is a sap-sucking insect, which can cause yellowing and debilitation in plants. It is suspected of being a vector of the 'Sudden Decline' disease that has decimated our cabbage trees in recent years. As its name implies it is often found on passion vines, where it can be present in considerable numbers. It also targets a number of other plants and trees such as privet and blackberries. The passion vine hopper eggs hatch in spring and the tiny nymph has a white, fluffy posterior, then from late January on it undergoes another moult and changes into a small, brown, smooth-winged adult. Adults, which survive until early winter, appear to queue in orderly fashion up plant stems. When disturbed both nymph and adult can spring from the plant.

Variegated spittle bug *Carystoterpa fingens* 6 mm

Family Cercopidae. The variegated spittle bug is a widespread native species, whose nymphs are found within frothy spittle-like masses, giving the insect its name. The froth is produced when the nymph ingests sap, which it then expels from its anus in the form of

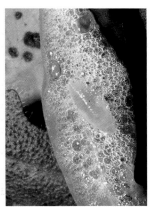

bubbles. This froth is sometimes called 'cuckoo spit', and helps protect the nymphs from predators. Both damselflies and some wasps, however, have been seen to breach the foam and drag the nymphs out. The adults are also sometimes called froghoppers and look rather like miniature cicadas.

Spittle bug nymphs in a frothy mass (meadow spittle bug, Philaenus spumarius*).*

Flat bug *Ctenoneurus hochstetteri* 9 mm

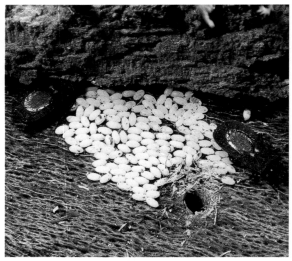

Flat bug adults with eggs.

Family Aradidae. The native flat bug is found throughout mainland New Zealand. Its preferred habitat is beneath the bark of dead trees and logs, and this is where it obtains its alternative name of bark bug. It is in these secluded areas that the adult finds fungi and moulds from which it sucks the juice, and it is here, too, that the female lays her eggs. There are several similar native flat bugs, such as *Ctenoneurus prendergrasti* and *C. myersi*, and all are very flat, dark brown or blackish bugs, with a distinctive 'doggy' smell.

Green shield bug *Nezara viridula* 16 mm

Green shield bug, adult.

Young green shield bug showing markings.

Family Pentatomidae. **Maori** kiri wenua kakariki. The green shield bug arrived from Britain late in the Second World War, and is now widespread. It is a serious garden pest and attacks a wide range of garden vegetables, but seems particularly partial to potatoes, peas, tomatoes and green beans. It produces a very strong

pungent smell when handled, which has earned it its alternative common name of stink bug. The young are beautifully patterned with green, black and white markings. There is a very similar native shield bug, the New Zealand vegetable bug (*Glaucias amyoti*; see illustration in Introduction, page 11.) It is a much more shiny, green insect which lacks the three white spots that the green shield bug has on its back.

Green shield bugs, newly hatched.

Cottony cushion scale *Icerya purchasi* 2 mm

Family Margarodidae. **Maori** kutu papa. Widespread in warmer regions of the world, the cottony cushion scale is an Australian introduction, found here from Mid Canterbury north to Northland. The immature cottony cushion scale debilitates plants by sucking out sap, and it excretes honeydew. The scale attacks a variety of plants and trees, including citrus, *Acacia* and gorse. The female produces a large, fluted, white egg case that remains attached to her body. The case increases in size as egg laying continues, and she is eventually incapacitated by it. Cottony cushion scale is preyed on by the cardinal ladybird (*Rodolia cardinalis*) and the steelblue ladybird (*Halmus chalybeus*; see page 66), and is parasitised by the small Australian fly *Cryptochaetum iceryyae*.

Megaloptera: dobsonflies

Dobsonflies are rather similar to stoneflies, but can be distinguished from these by their two pairs of large, rather similar wings which are held tent-like over the body when the dobsonfly is at rest. Those of the stoneflies, on the other hand, are rolled neatly back against the body. Dobsonflies also lack the large cerci (tail filaments) sported by the plecopterans. All dobsonfly nymphs are aquatic. The adults do not feed, and they stay close to the water where they are often preyed upon by fish and insects such as dragonflies. Dobsonflies are the most primitive of the holometabolous orders. They are found only in North America, Asia and Australasia, with just a single species in New Zealand.

Dobsonfly *Archichauliodes diversus* 22 mm

Family Corydalidae. **Maori** ngaro parirau. There is only one dobsonfly species in New Zealand, found along most fast-flowing streams and rivers throughout the country, as this is the habitat in which the female prefers to lay her eggs. These are deposited on rocks emerging from streams and the hatching larvae drop into the water. Here they remain for several years, going through several moults. The larva eats other aquatic insects, particularly mayfly nymphs, and its powerful jaws have earned it the name 'toe biter'. Once mature, the larva burrows under stones for a four-month pre-pupal stage, before a three-week pupation from which the adult emerges. Adults live only a few days.

Neuroptera: antlions, lacewings

A defining characteristic of these insects is their two pairs of delicate, gauzy wings, which have a dense network of cross veins. At rest these wings are held tent-like above the body in a fashion similar to that of the dobsonflies (see previous entry). Neuropterans are also superficially similar to damselflies, but can be separated on closer inspection. The adults are short-legged and have sensory spots on their wings. Neuropterans are holometabolous. There are about 5000 species worldwide with 16 in New Zealand.

Antlion *Weeleus acutus* 30 mm

Family Myrmeleontidae. **Maori** kutu kutu. The native antlion, which somewhat resembles a dobsonfly in appearance, is widespread throughout mainland New Zealand, though is more sporadic in some areas than others. The insect gets its common name from the fascinating hunting habits of its larva. This digs cone-shaped holes in loose, dry, friable soil in sheltered positions such as those afforded by clay banks, trees and even old buildings. Here it lurks, buried in the bottom of the hole, with just its jaws exposed. When prey such as slaters, spiders or ants wander past, they sometimes fall into the hole, to be grabbed by the antlion.

Tasmanian lacewing *Micromus tasmaniae* 5 mm

Family Hemerobiidae. Sometimes also known as the brown lacewing, or aphid-lion, this Australian species is widespread throughout most of mainland New Zealand, from sea level to medium altitudes. Both the adults and larvae are enthusiastic predators of aphids,

mealybugs and other insects. The larva has conspicuous calliper-like jaws which it uses to seize and hold prey while sucking out the body contents. The adult is mostly nocturnal, and the female deposits eggs on the stems of plants, with the larvae pupating under bark or leaves, including those of aphid-infested roses.

Coleoptera: beetles

Beetles are defined as insects with biting mouthparts and with hardened forewings called elytra (singular: elytron), which cover and protect the membranous, veined hind wings. They are the largest insect group with around 400,000 species so far described, which is about 25 per cent of all known animals. There are approximately 5500 species so far described from New Zealand, and around 90 per cent of these are native. Most beetle families are represented here; however, families like the stag beetles, ladybirds and jewel beetles, although present, have relatively few species in New Zealand. Many are flightless and large, a product of New Zealand's long isolation and paucity of predators. Beetle eggs are often laid in tree wood, often in living trees, but also in dead or dying trees, with grubs hatching to consume the wood. The wood-boring activities of some beetles in living trees make them a pest. Depending on species, beetle adults consume a variety of food, including foliage, nectar, mildew, fungi, or other animals such as aphids and scale insects.

The beetles include ladybirds, which were known as the 'beetle of Our Lady' during the Middle Ages, a name which was eventually shortened to ladybird. About 5000 species are known worldwide, of which New Zealand has about 40, about half of them natives. The most commonly encountered ones are exotic. Depending on the species, ladybird adults and larvae feed on aphids, mealybugs, scale insects, insect eggs and some small, soft-bodied insects.

Burnt pine longhorn *Arhopalus tristis* 35 mm

Family Cerambycidae. This beetle was first noticed in New Zealand in the 1950s, having been accidentally introduced from Europe in cable drum battens. From its first colonisation site in Northland, it has spread as far south as Canterbury and Westland. Although it is found in most of our exotic pine species, it is not considered to be a major pest, as it prefers to lay its eggs on dead or dying trees. It has been known to deposit its eggs on trees within 24 hours of a forest fire, and this is where its common name originates. It has shorter antennae than most other longhorn beetles now found in New Zealand.

Squeaking longhorn *Hexatricha pulverulenta* 20 mm

Family Cerambycidae. **Maori** tataka. The squeaking longhorn is an attractive native species, widely distributed in the North and South Islands. It has now made the move from native hardwoods into exotic conifer forests. As it attacks only dead or dying trees, it is not considered a threat. However, countries such as China insist that it not be imported into that country in timber or logs and this means that these products have to be fumigated here at considerable expense. As its name indicates, this beetle makes a squeaking noise when it is handled by rubbing its thorax against a roughened portion of the elytra. The grubs are parasitised by the lemon tree borer parasite (*Xanthocryptus novozealandicus*; see page 131).

Striped longhorn *Coptomma lineatum* 20 mm

Family Cerambycidae. **Maori** tataka. This native beetle is also sometimes called the candy-striped longhorn. It is restricted to the North Island, where it is of concern to both nursery owners and foresters as it bores into the branches, twigs and terminal shoots of a number of trees and shrubs, both native and exotic. The adults emerge in late spring and early summer, and feed on pollen. Like those of the squeaking longhorn (see previous entry), larvae are parasitised by the lemon tree borer parasite (*Xanthocryptus novozealandicus*; see page 131). The striped longhorn can be confused with its relative, *Coptomma sticticum*, but the cream-coloured stripes on *C. sticticum* are not as regular, nor as pronounced.

Lemon tree borer *Oemona hirta* 25 mm

Family Cerambycidae. A native species, the lemon tree borer occurs throughout the North Island and in Nelson in the South Island. Despite its common name, it doesn't confine itself to lemon trees. The larva also bores into the wood of native shrubs and trees such as mahoe, rangiora and tarata. It is sometimes a considerable pest in citrus trees and vineyards, and also attacks shelter belts such as *Hakea* and poplars. The female lays eggs into the soft tissue of the trunk, so the larvae are normally deep inside the wood of their hosts; hence they are difficult to control by chemical means. The rather plain adult emerges in late summer and autumn. The beetle is parasitised by the lemon tree borer parasite (*Xanthocryptus novozealandicus*; see page 131).

Huhu beetle *Prionoplus reticularis* 45 mm

Family Cerambycidae. **Maori** tunga rere. The native huhu beetle is New Zealand's largest and heaviest beetle, and as it is attracted to lights it is hard to overlook as it bumbles noisily about when it emerges

in midsummer. It is widespread throughout both main islands and the fat larvae, which were eaten by Maori, can be found in dead rimu, kauri, kahikatea and matai trees but more abundantly in radiata pine. The adult squeaks when handled, and is capable of giving a sharp nip. The other Maori name for this beetle is pepe te muimui, but the larvae were called huhu. There is a similar species, the large *Xixuthrus microcerus*, whose grubs are harvested by Aboriginals in Queensland.

Flower longhorn *Zorion guttigerum* 6 mm

Family Cerambycidae. It is a bit of a pity that these beetles are so small, as the native *Zorion* longhorns are probably the most colourful of our insects.

They are common throughout New Zealand and the larvae, which live under the bark of trees, are particularly prolific on shelter-belt cuttings. Once the adult emerges, it is often encountered feeding on the nectar and pollen of a wide variety of trees, both native and exotic. Ten species have been described so far, some of which, such as *Zorion taranakiensis* and *Z. kaikouraiensis*, are fairly restricted in range, with one species, *Z. opacum*, being known only from the Chatham Islands.

Burnished beech beetle *Chalcodrya variegata* 20 mm

Family Chalcodryidae. This species is of particular interest to entomologists as the genus *Chalcodrya*, along with the two related genera, *Philpottia* and *Onysius*, was once considered to belong to a family that was endemic to New Zealand. Recently, however, related beetles have turned up in Chile, Argentina and the Falklands, which is another indicator of the ancient Gondwanaland connections. The burnished beech beetle is found throughout the two main islands, from sea level to about 1000 m, in a variety of trees and shrubs, but more particularly in beech forest. The larval stage is not known.

Mealybug ladybird *Cryptolaemus montrouzieri* 6 mm

Family Coccinellidae. **Maori** mumutawa. The mealybug ladybird was deliberately introduced from Australia in 1897 and in the 1920s to act as a biological control agent. As its name indicates, this

ladybird is a major predator of the longtailed mealybug (*Pseudococcus longispinus*), which the larva (pictured here) closely resembles in appearance. The adult is a typical ladybird in shape with a uniformly black carapace and an orange-red thorax. It first became established in the Auckland and Northland areas, but it has since started to move south and is now found in both the Bay of Plenty and Poverty Bay.

Steelblue ladybird *Halmus chalybeus* 5 mm

Family Coccinellidae. **Maori** mumutawa. This Australian ladybird was introduced to New Zealand in 1899 and 1905 to control scale insects that infest citrus orchards, in particular the black scale (*Saissetia oleae*) and the cottony cushion scale (*Icerya purchasi*; see page 58), but it also preys on aphids. It is now commonly found from Nelson northwards, in both gardens and native bush, but it occurs more generally when citrus trees are nearby. In certain lights it can appear green in colour. Like some other ladybird species, it can exude drops of a bitter yellowish-orange liquid from the joints of its legs, which makes it distasteful to birds.

Large-spotted ladybird *Harmonia conformis* 8 mm

Family Coccinellidae. **Maori** papapa kopure. The Australian large-spotted ladybird is now an important biological controller of pests, such as aphids and scale insects. It is also known as the 18-spotted ladybird, but if you look carefully you will see it has 20 spots. It is most common in the north of the North Island. The large-spotted ladybird has a close New Zealand relative, *Harmonia antipoda*, a ladybird with mottled black-and-yellow elytra, which is most often found on acacia trees. Both *H. conformis* and *H. antipoda* prey on the eggs of the eucalyptus tortoise beetle (*Paropsis charybdis*; see page 71), a pest in exotic forestry blocks.

Fungus-eating ladybird *Illeus galbula* 5 mm

Fungus-eating ladybird, adult with larvae.

Family Coccinellidae. **Maori** mumutawa. Introduced from Australia, this yellow-and-black ladybird has a pattern on its back that has been likened to the comic character Batman. Larvae and adults feed on powdery mildew, a fungus which often attacks the leaves of vegetables, such as pumpkins and courgettes, and dahlias. The fungus-eating ladybird adult is an active and fast flier. The larva, creamy white with rows of black dots, likewise can run quickly. The pupa, also whitish with lines of black dots, is also quite active, and when disturbed will stand up on its end.

Giraffe weevil *Lasiorhynchus barbicornis* 70 mm

George Gibbs

Giraffe weevil, female.

Family Brentidae. **Maori** tuwhaipapa. The native giraffe weevil is found throughout mainland New Zealand, wherever its host trees are found: native softwoods such as kauri, tawa, rewarewa, karaka and pukatea. The female lays her eggs in dead or dying parts of these trees and it takes two years for larvae to develop and pupate and adults to emerge. The adult insect lives only a few weeks and is an ungainly flier. The giraffe weevil differs from true weevils in lacking 'elbows' on its antennae, and it is relatively unusual in New Zealand for being sexually dimorphic. (The antennae of the male are positioned at the tip of the rostrum, whereas those of the female sit further back; this is possibly an adaptation to her role of ovipositing, which she performs with the rostrum.) The giraffe weevil holds two records: it is our longest beetle and the world's longest weevil.

Speargrass weevil *Lyperobius barbarae* 25 mm

Family Curculionidae. The native speargrass weevil was discovered relatively recently, and has been found only in higher altitude areas of Central Otago. Its biology is not well known, but it is thought to be similar to that of the other speargrass weevils. In these, both larvae and adults feed on the speargrasses (genus *Aciphylla*; as pictured) common in many of the ungrazed and unburnt fellfield (1200–2000 m) areas of the South Island (except for *Lyperobius huttoni*, which can be found almost at sea level on the Wellington coast, though at higher altitudes in the South Island). The female lays eggs in the spring and the larval stage lasts about a year. Similar, more widely spread species are the giant black-and-white weevil (*L. hudsoni*) and the giant alpine weevil (*L. spedeni*).

George Gibbs

Island weevil *Lyperopais alternans* 20 mm

George Gibbs

Family Curculionidae. The native island weevil is a rare weevil that has been collected only from sites in Fiordland in subalpine *Chionochloa* and *Dracophyllum* grassland. It is a local representative of a large, diverse and striking sub-family of weevils, the Entiminae. Before the Polynesian rat or kiore arrived, these weevils were here in large numbers. Now, unfortunately, most species are confined to rat-free islands and upland grasslands with a few being also found in *Astelia* and flaxes.

White-fringed weevil *Naupactus leucoloma* 12 mm

Family Curculionidae. The white-fringed weevil originally hails from South America, from where it was introduced into the United States. From there it came to New Zealand during the Second World

War among military equipment, arriving first in Hawke's Bay. It has now colonised most of the North Island and the South Island south to about Canterbury. It is a general feeder and causes damage to pastures, wheat and barley crops, and exotic conifer seedlings. It also targets garden vegetables including brassicas, pumpkins, tomatoes, potatoes and vines. It is flightless and parthenogenetic, and during its relatively short lifespan it lays several hundred eggs. The common name refers to the pale band that runs along its body.

Two-spined weevil *Nyxetes bidens* 14 mm

Family Curculionidae. **Maori** papapa ihu. The native two-spined weevil is the sole member of its genus. It is widespread throughout both main islands and it can often be encountered in summer feeding on pollen and nectar, which it harvests from a wide range of flowers, both native and exotic. It seems to be particularly partial to the blossoms of our native palm, the nikau, as well as those of hebes. The grub feeds in vines and branches and by doing this, it causes the plant to produce lumps, called galls, in which it feeds. The two sharp spines with which this weevil is equipped probably serve as a deterrent to birds.

Large pintail beetle *Mordella antarctica* 22 mm

Family Mordellidae. This native wedge-shaped beetle comes equipped with a spine-like spring on its tail that gives the insect momentum if it needs to take off in a hurry. It occurs in many localities in the North Island, but so far does not seem to be recorded from the South Island. The large pintail beetle can often be seen visiting a variety of flowers, with a preference for manuka and rata. On these trees can sometimes also be found its close relative *Mordella detracta*. The two species are easily distinguished as *M. detracta* is much smaller, with two large white spots on the rear part of its elytra.

Eucalyptus tortoise beetle *Paropsis charybdis* 14 mm

Family Chrysomelidae. The eucalyptus tortoise beetle arrived here from Australia about 1916, when it was first noticed in the Lyttelton area. At first it spread slowly through the South Island and then much more rapidly once it reached the North Island. It attacks a number of eucalypt (gum) trees but is more prevalent in Tasmanian blue gum, mountain ash and shining gum. The eucalyptus tortoise beetle damages these trees by eating their leaves. The southern ladybird (*Cleobora mellyi*) was introduced as  a biological control, but this seems to have been only a limited success as it has established itself only in the Marlborough area. Of more use has been species of large-spotted ladybird (*Harmonia conformis* and *H. antipoda*), which prey on the eucalyptus tortoise beetle's eggs. The eucalyptus tortoise beetle hibernates in winter under the bark of its host trees.

Grass grub *Costelytra zealandica* 10 mm

Family Scarabaeidae. **Maori** tutaeruru. This is a widespread native chafer, the adults of which form large, noisy swarms on summer nights. These consume vast amounts of the foliage of trees and shrubs and are a serious pest in parts of Canterbury, Otago and Southland where the larvae (shown above) feed on grass roots, thus damaging pasture. The larva pupates underground and larvae often emerge in dense swarms usually from October to December for the main flight period, peaking in November in Canterbury. Several other chafers are considered to be pasture pests, including two introduced species, the Tasmanian grass grub (*Acrossidius tasmaniae*) and the black beetle (*Heteronychus arator*), which arrived in the 1930s from South Africa.

Large sand scarab *Pericoptus truncatus* 30 mm

Large sand scarab beetle, adult.

Family Scarabaeidae. **Maori** ngungutawa. The native large sand scarab is quite common in dunes from Canterbury northwards. The adult spends daylight buried in the sand, emerging at night to fly noisily around in search of mates and food. The trails it leaves in the sand are quite obvious early in the

Large sand scarab beetle, larva.

morning, as it also spends much time walking about. The female lays eggs deep in the sand and the large white grubs can often be located in the sand under driftwood, though they feed on the roots of dune plants. Recently an exotic scolid wasp, the yellow flower wasp (*Radumeris tasmaniensis*), has arrived in the Far North and is causing concern by parasitising the large sand scarab larvae. The female stings and paralyses the scarab larva and lays eggs on it. The wasp larva then slowly consumes the paralysed beetle larva. A related but very similar native scarab is *Pericoptus punctatus*, which is a somewhat smaller species. Another native sand scarab of particular interest is *P. frontalis*. This favours the sandy areas provided by river-banks and sand bars in inland Otago.

Manuka chafer *Pyronota festiva* 10 mm

Family Scarabaeidae. **Maori** kekerewai. This native chafer is widespread in forested areas of both main islands. It occurs in several colours, mostly green, blue and orange, but with black individuals being not uncommon at higher altitudes. As its name implies, the adult feeds on the flowers of manuka trees, but the larva eats grass roots. In summer the adult forms part of the diet of smaller native birds and often falls into streams where it is taken by kokopu (*Galaxias* species) and trout. Maori once baked this beetle with the pollen of raupo (bulrushes) to make a type of bread.

Tanguru chafer *Stethaspis suturalis* 24 mm

Family Scarabaeidae. **Maori** kekerewai. The native tanguru chafer is common throughout New Zealand's three main islands, in both native and exotic forest. On quiet evenings at dusk this beetle can be heard buzzing about. The large grubs, called papahu by Maori, feed on tree roots. Another green chafer which could be confused with this one is the native mumu chafer (*Stethaspis longicornis*), but this lacks the faint yellow band that runs down the tanguru chafer's back. The manuka chafer (*Pyronota festiva*; see previous entry), could also be confused with the tanguru chafer, but is a much smaller beetle, with variable colouration.

74

Stinking ground beetle *Plocamostethus planiusculus* 25 mm

Beetles of various species are frequently infested with mites.

Family Carabidae. **Maori** kurikuri. The native stinking ground beetle is widespread from the Coromandel Peninsula to Nelson-Marlborough in wet forests extending to alpine zones, in pine plantations, scrubland, pasture and fellfields. This flightless carabid beetle often shelters under logs during the day, and at night is very active, searching out its insect prey. It can give a sharp nip when handled. A further defence is the powerful stench that it emits, from which it gets its Maori name, which means dog-like. It is one of our 424 or so carabid beetles, all of which look rather similar, most being flattish, shiny black beetles; one exception is the metallic green ground beetle (see next entry).

Metallic green ground beetle *Megadromus antarcticus* 30 mm

Family Carabidae. **Maori** kurikuri. The native metallic green ground beetle is found mostly in Canterbury but occasionally occurs in other parts of the South Island in gardens and drier scrubland. Most of New Zealand's carabid beetles look rather similar, the majority being flattish, shiny black beetles; the metallic green ground, however, is an attractive bronzy-black, with brilliant metallic green reflections. It is flightless but capable of defending itself with a powerful bite and offensive smell. This does not deter animals like moreporks and hedgehogs, which are known to eat this beetle. A closely related species is *Megadromus vigil*, a shiny bluish-black beetle, common in the Wellington area.

75

Seashore carabid beetle *Brullea antarctica* 30 mm

Family Carabidae. **Maori** mumutawa pango. The native seashore carabid beetle is rather uncommonly encountered. It is nocturnal, lives in sand and lays its eggs in burrows up to 11 cm deep. Occa-

sionally the adult is seen wandering on the beach in daytime after heavy rain and high tide. Specimens have been collected from the Far North to Fiordland; the specimen shown was photographed near Westport. It is a very robust beetle, and its short, sturdy legs makes one think of steroid users. It is found in sandy areas, in and around driftwood and stones, just above the high-tide mark. Near Otaki it was observed that this beetle was being preyed upon by the native katipo spider. It was first described by the splendidly named Frenchman, Count François Laporte de Castlenau.

Tiger beetle *Cicindela waiouraensis* 12 mm

Family Carabidae. **Maori** papapa. Around a dozen species of tiger beetles, genus *Cicindela*, have been described from New Zealand, of which *C. waiourensis* (pictured), is one of the scarcer ones, restricted as it is to mid-altitude areas in the central North Island. At lower altitudes in the North Island it is replaced by *C. tuberculata*, which is slightly smaller and not as distinctly marked. In the South Island, the most common species is *C. latecincta*. The tiger beetle adult frequents open, sunny situations and, although it can fly, it prefers to run its victims down. The larva hatches in the ground and lives in holes, about 10–15 cm deep, for about a year. It thrusts its head out to seize an unwary insect with its jaws.

Redwinged lycid beetle *Porrostoma rufipenne* 15 mm

Family Lycidae. The redwinged lycid beetle is an Australian species that is now well established in the North Island and in Nelson
in the South Island from where it seems to be extending its range
southwards. The adult can often be seen on warm summer days,
visiting flowers to harvest nectar and pollen. Its distinctive black-
and-red colouration indicates to predators that it may be distasteful,
and overseas a range of insects, including wasps, flies, moths and
beetles, use a similar form of mimicry. The larva lives under the bark
of fallen trees. About 3500 species of lycid occur worldwide, mostly
in the tropics, but this is the sole New Zealand example.

Helm's stag beetle *Geodorcus helmsi* 42 mm

George Gibbs

Family Lucanidae. The native Helm's stag beetle is a large and
spectacular species, found along the western length of the South
Island but more abundant in the high-rainfall areas of South
Westland, Fiordland and Stewart Island, where rats are not too
numerous. Here the adult can often be found around kahikatea
and rimu trees, where it feeds on the tree sap and shelters on the
ground, under logs. The female (pictured) lays eggs in rotten wood
where the larva takes several years to develop. There are several other
Geodorcus species, all of which are rare and restricted in range and
a number of which are protected by law.

77

Brown stag beetle *Syndesus cornutus* 25 mm

Family Lucanidae. The brown stag beetle is also sometimes known as the Australian stag beetle, as it originates from Tasmania. It was first noticed here in 1961 in Gisborne and Auckland, and has spread fairly widely throughout the North Island. Stag beetles are noted for the male's large jaws, or mandibles, which it uses when fighting rival males. This characteristic is not so obvious in this species, but is pronounced in some tropical species and in the New Zealand genus *Geodorcus*. The female has shorter mandibles. The brown stag beetle adult spends the day under the bark of trees, emerging at night to feed on tree sap and fruit sap. It prefers damp conditions and the beetle is not generally encountered in drier areas. The larva lives in rotting wood.

Mecoptera: scorpionflies

Although there are 500 species of scorpionfly, only a single species is found here. This is often omitted from New Zealand insect books, which is a pity as it is an intriguing insect. The scorpionfly gets its common name from the male's habit of carrying its genitalia curved upwards over its back. It was among the earliest of the holometabolous insects to evolve. Mating in the Mecoptera is especially fascinating as it is a very complex procedure, which, depending on the genus, can involve the male attracting a female with his pheromone, then offering the female a food gift which she feeds on during copulation. Another option is called forced copulation; a male using this strategy doesn't emit any pheromones or supply any food but simply rushes at the female and attempts to mate, often successfully.

Scorpionfly *Nannochorista philpotti* 10 mm

George Gibbs

Scorpionfly, adult male.

Family Choristidae. The native scorpionfly is widespread throughout the South Island and Stewart Island, but does not as yet seem to have been collected in the North Island. It occurs in a variety of aquatic habitats from lowland areas to medium altitudes, but seems to have a preference for slow-moving, muddy-bottomed streams when laying eggs. It is one of the only scorpionfly species in the world to have fully aquatic larvae, which feed on midge larvae, taking about a year to fully mature. These are also unusual among aquatic larvae in that they have compound eyes. This scorpionfly has related genera in southern Australia and South America.

Diptera: true flies

Diptera is a huge and amazingly diverse group of insects, the best known of which, unfortunately, tend to be pests like the mosquitoes, sandflies, house flies and blowflies. However, there are also many flies that are beneficial and attractive. Although many insects are called flies, such as butterflies, dragonflies, scorpionflies and so on, the true flies can be recognised and separated from the others by having only a single pair of wings (when they have them), with their rear wings having being replaced by a pair of balancing organs called halteres. Flies have a holometabolous lifestyle with the egg hatching into a small grub-like creature, often called a maggot, which progresses through three moults until it pupates and the adult emerges.

Large predacious hoverfly, Melangyna novaezelandiae
(see page 84).

Giant crane fly *Austrotipula hudsoni* 45 mm

Family Tipulidae. **Maori** matua waeroa rere. This is the world's largest fly family, with 15,000 species recognised. About 570 species of crane fly are known to live in New Zealand, and the native giant crane fly is one of the largest. The Maori name means chief of the mosquitoes. However, unlike mosquitoes, crane flies are inoffensive insects, with the females feeding solely on nectar. It is common from Rotorua southwards and favours wet forests, where it is particularly obvious after rain. The larvae, called leatherjackets, live in moist areas, buried in the mud. Crane flies are also called daddy longlegs but the true daddy longlegs is a spider (*Pholcus phalangioides*). The crane fly adult is preyed upon by native insectivores such as dragonflies and wasps, and also by introduced vespulid wasps.

Orange crane fly *Leptotarsus clarus* 15 mm

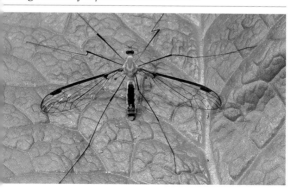

Family Tipulidae. **Maori** matua waeroa rere. The native orange crane fly is known only from the North Island, where it is particularly prevalent after rain, sometimes occurring in swarms. It resembles a mosquito somewhat in shape, with its thin body and long trailing legs. The maggots live in damp soil where they feed on decaying vegetation. Other commonly encountered New Zealand crane flies in this genus are the native *Leptotarsus binotatus*, a common bush dweller, and the alpine species *L. montanus*.

DIPTERA

Macromastix *species.*

Family Tipulidae. **Maori** matua waeroa rere. The native net-winged crane fly is one of our more common crane flies, occurring fairly widely in the three main islands. It is particularly common after rain when it congregates in dense swarms in late summer. It is a typical crane fly in shape, with long, slender legs and attenuated body. The legs are commonly described as 'deciduous', in that they are easily damaged and readily break off. The adult is not a strong flier and is often preyed upon by native and introduced predatory insects and birds. Other commonly encountered native crane flies include *Aphrophila neozelandica*, common along stony streams throughout the country; and *Zelandotipula fulva*, which is equally widespread.

Three-lined hoverfly *Helophilus trilineatus* 16 mm

Family Syrphidae. **Maori** ngaro tara. Those flies that we generally refer to as hoverflies are sometimes known overseas as flower flies; a number of species are referred to as drone flies. The native three-lined hoverfly occurs throughout the country and often ventures indoors. It is a very rapid flier, darting from place to place, and then hovering over flowers, feeding on pollen and nectar, and so aiding pollination. The adult is a very skilful flier and even mates in the air. The eggs are laid in still water, which is often polluted or stagnant, usually near, or in, decaying material, where the maggot hatches and lies buried in the substrate. It obtains oxygen from the water surface by extending a long breathing tube or 'rat-tail', earning it the name rat-tailed maggot.

Small predacious hoverfly *Melanostoma fasciatum* 15 mm

Family Syrphidae. **Maori** ngaro tara. This native hover-fly is widespread throughout New Zealand and is par-ticularly common around orchards, vineyards and cereal crops. The adult female lays eggs on plants that have high numbers of aphids, which provide a  source of food for the maggots. The adult, like other hoverflies, feeds on nectar and pollen, and often can be seen in summer hover-ing over flowers and flowering grass stems. The maggot, however, is predatory, and is an important biological control of a number of pests, in particular, aphids, small caterpillars and mealybugs. The small predacious hoverfly is being trialled in Italy and Switzerland to see if it is as effective there in controlling pests, while a related species, *Melanostoma agrolas*, from Pakistan, is being considered for introduction here.

Large predacious hoverfly *Melangyna novaezelandiae* 20 mm

Family Syrphidae. **Maori** ngaro tara. The large predacious hoverfly is a widespread native insect that is common in many parts of the three main islands. The adult lives largely on nectar and pollen, and it provides an important service as a plant pollinator. This hoverfly

is one of the most common pollinators of our alpine flowers and in summer it can be seen over these plants, hovering helicopter-like before departing at high speed. The maggot, on the other hand, is insectivorous and is an important biological control of scale insects and aphids, as well as the larvae of the introduced diamondback moth (*Plutella xylostella*), a pest in brassica crops. A rather similar species to *Melangyna novaezelandiae* is *M. viridiceps*, but this later hoverfly, an Australian species, is greener in colour.

Narcissus bulb fly *Merodon equestris* 14 mm

Family Syrphidae. **Maori** ngaro paira. The narcissus bulb fly, a hoverfly, arrived here fairly early after European colonisation, and is now found in just about any place in the country where daffodils and narcissus grow. The adult is very hairy and closely resembles a bumblebee and no doubt this mimicry helps to protect the narcissus bulb fly from predatory birds. It also produces a loud buzzing sound which also perhaps assists this subterfuge. In spring, after the daffodils have died back, this hoverfly visits the hole exposed by the dead foliage, and lays a single egg. The hatching maggot completely destroys the bulb. Like other hoverflies, this is a particularly strong flier.

Red-headed soldier fly *Inopus rubriceps* 10 mm

Freshly emerged adult, with wings not yet fully expanded.

Family Stratiomyidae. Also called the Australian soldier fly, this species is quite common around gardens in northern areas, having arrived in New Zealand from Australia in the 1940s. In summer, and all year round in warmer areas, it can be seen sunbathing on the leaves and branches of garden plants. Although the adult is short-lived and non-feeding, its grub is a pest on pasture and maize crops. Other commonly seen soldier flies are the garden soldier fly (*Exaireta spinigera*), which arrived here early last century; and the American soldier fly (see next entry). Our most common native soldier fly is *Odontomyia chloris* (see page 87), which has a broad green-and-black abdomen. The name soldier fly refers to the bright metallic colours of some of the overseas species.

American soldier fly *Hermetia illucens* 20 mm

Family Stratiomyidae. The American soldier fly first arrived here in the 1950s and is now found throughout most of the north of the North Island. The adult feeds on flowers and often ventures indoors in summer. It is not a strong flier and can often be seen sunning itself on the ground. The eggs are laid in compost heaps and among rotting plants. This soldier fly can be distinguished from the rather similar garden soldier fly (*Exaireta spinigera*), which arrived here last century, by the two conspicuous white patches on the front of its abdomen. With its narrow waist, it looks something like a wasp.

Green soldier fly *Beris lacuans* 12 mm

A native (green) soldier fly, Beris lacuans.

Green soldier fly, Odontomyia chloris.

Family Stratiomyidae. **Maori** namu. This native soldier fly is common in many parts of both main islands of New Zealand, and in summer the adult can often be seen visiting flowers where it feeds on pollen. When at rest it folds its wings one on top of the other. The maggot, which is pale and fat, can often be found in rotting vegetation as well as in compost heaps. There are a number of very similar species so the identification should only be regarded as provisional.

DIPTERA

Robber fly, Neoitamus varius.

Robber fly, N. melanopogon.

Family Asilidae. **Maori** ngaro. A number of native *Neoitamus* species are found in New Zealand, including *N. varius* and *N. melanopogon.* The adults are common in clearings in forested areas in both the North and South Islands. New Zealand has only a few species of robber flies, but as they are all large and conspicuous they are easily seen. They are skilled hunters and usually perch quietly on vegetation waiting for their prey to fly past, which they then dart out and grab. They are non-selective in their choice of victims, even taking on bees and wasps (by grabbing with their legs and biting), and have also sometimes been observed attacking web-building spiders. Their larvae, which develop in soft wood and mud, are also general feeders but often prey on the larvae of other insect species. Other commonly encountered native species are *Neoitamus smithi* and *N. walkeri.* The robber flies are sometimes also known as bee killers and assassin flies.

Robber fly, N. varius, *facial detail.*

Green longlegged fly *Parentia malitiosa* 5 mm

Family Dolichopodidae. Dolichopodid flies are plentiful in New Zealand, but not a lot is known about them. Some of the most common are the beautiful metallic green species, such as the native green longlegged fly pictured here, but bronze and blue species are also often seen. In warmer weather they can often be seen sunning themselves on leaves or darting about searching for small insects. Not all species are insectivorous, and some feed on nectar. However,

the larvae are all believed to eat the larvae of other insects. We have 27 species of *Parentia*, and among the more colourful are *P. pukakiensis*, *P. titirangi* and *P. aotearoa*.

Australian leafroller tachinid fly *Trigonospila brevifacies* 8 mm

Family Tachinidae. This is one of the world's largest fly families with about 8000 species, of which New Zealand has over 100. The Australian leafroller tachinid fly, now established widely in central and northern New Zealand, specialises in parasitising caterpillars of the various species of leafroller moths in the Tortri-

cidae family. When introduced, its main target was the light brown apple moth (*Epiphyas postvittana*). It thus provides a service to orchardists, as some exotic leafrollers, such as the codling moth (*Cydia pomonella*), are pests of pip-fruit. However, the tachinid also attacks or parasitises the harmless native species of leafroller and other small moths, but little is known about its impact on these.

89

Bush gadfly *Scaptia adrel* 16 mm

Family Tabanidae. **Maori** rango. The native bush gadfly is mostly a forest dweller, and it can often be seen resting on tree trunks. The adult usually inhabits clearings or the bush edge, and is often seen on flowers, particularly those of manuka. The maggot lives in damp soil and is predatory. It is a member of a very large family of flies, with over 4000 species so far described worldwide, of which we have some 20. In the various countries in which it is found,

the family goes by a variety of names, such as tabanids, horseflies, gadflies, deer flies or clegs. They all share the same distinguishing characteristic of having large, reflective, iridescent eyes, and all have a prominent proboscis. In tropical countries some tabanid flies are serious pests, as the females target horses, goats, cattle and even humans, when they are searching for blood with which to nourish eggs. Fortunately, none of these bloodthirsty species are found here. All our tabanid flies are nectar eaters.

Brown blowfly *Calliphora stygia* 10 mm

Family Calliphoridae. **Maori** rango tuamaro. This blowfly arrived from Australia with the early European settlers and is wide-spread throughout the country, but is more common in lowland areas. As it causes fly-strike by laying its eggs on live sheep, where they become maggots, thus 'blowing' the flesh, it is of concern to farmers, as the maggots on hatching bore into their hosts

to feed, causing sores that become infected. There are over 2500 species of calliphorid flies worldwide with some 40 occurring here, including the native New Zealand bluebottle (*Calliphora quadrimaculata*), the golden-haired blowfly (*C. laemica*) from Australia and the European blowfly (*C. vicina*; see next entry). They all venture indoors in summer, making a loud buzzing sound. A rather pretty blowfly is the native kelp bluebottle (*Xenocalliphora hortoni*), which lives on decaying seaweed.

European blowfly *Calliphora vicina* 16 mm

Cuni de Graaf

Family Calliphoridae. This blowfly arrived in New Zealand along with the early European settlers and is now widespread throughout the North and South Islands. It is a cold-hardy species, often surviving over winter and being among the earliest blowflies to appear in spring, attracted to houses by the smell of cooking. The adult can often be seen sunbathing on sunny walls. The female lays 300 to 600 eggs on dead animals and food scraps. Before antibiotics, maggots of this blowfly were used for cleaning infected wounds. The native New Zealand blue blowfly (rango pango, *Calliphora quadrimaculata*) is rather similar to this species but is a darker purplish-blue in colour. This latter species is also sometimes called the bluebottle.

91

Greenbottle *Lucilia sericata* 10 mm

Cuni de Graaf

Introduced greenbottle, Lucilia sericata.

Cuni de Graaf

Hairy maggot blowfly, Chrysomya rufifacies.

Family Calliphoridae. The introduced greenbottle first arrived here in the late 19th century. It is variable in colour, ranging from bluish-green to copper, and these colours darken as the fly gets older. As the adult feeds on flowers it is seldom found indoors. The maggot is, by contrast, carnivorous. The female lays her eggs, which can be as many as 6000 in number, on sheep and goats, and when the maggots hatch they burrow into the animal's flesh, causing 'fly-strike'. A related species, the Australian sheep blowfly (*Lucilia cuprina*), arrived here in the 1970s and is also a serious livestock pest. The two species are difficult to tell apart, but the sheep blowfly tends to have a more bronzy appearance. The introduced hairy maggot blowfly (*Chrysomya rufifacies*) is distinguished from the introduced greenbottle by its larger size and more distinctive markings.

Bat-winged fly *Exsul singularis* 14 mm

Family Muscidae. Although regarded as rare, the native bat-winged fly is only infrequently encountered, as it lives at high altitudes in remote areas. Here it lives in sunny, open areas from the Paparoa Range south to Fiordland, where it is to be seen along the banks of fast-flowing streams. Although a rather clumsy flier,

Brian Patrick

the adult preys on emerging aquatic insects, which it seizes and devours on the wing. It has also been seen hunting down moths and butterflies. The larval stage is not known. It has been called the bat-winged cannibal fly but there is no evidence that it preys on its own species. Like many alpine insects, it basks in the sun on rocks, its large dark wings absorbing the heat rather like solar panels.

European flesh fly *Sarcophaga crassipalpis* 15 mm

Family Sarcophagidae. **Maori** ngaro. No one is sure where this species originated from, and it is almost cosmopolitan in distribution, being widespread throughout Europe and the Middle East. It is now established in farms and gardens throughout the North Island, where it can often be found in the vicinity of rubbish dumps and compost heaps. The European flesh fly gives birth to living maggots, which it drops into compost, manure and on to living and dead animals. It is of some service as the maggots clean up carrion.

Cuni de Graaf

Australian striped mosquito *Ochlerotatus notoscriptus* 6 mm

The itching and swelling of a mosquito bite is caused by the female's saliva, which she injects into the bite to serve as an anticoagulant.

Family Culicidae. **Maori** waeroa. New Zealand is home to 16 mosquito species, of which four are introduced. The Australian striped mosquito (*Ochlerotatus notoscriptus*) haunts bush, urban parks and gardens in discrete locations from Northland south to Christchurch. Flying between dawn and dusk, it is silent in flight, readily bites humans and other mammals and may transmit heartworm to dogs. The southern saltmarsh mosquito (*O. camptorhynchus*) has appeared in parts of the North Island since 1998, and can transmit Ross River virus. Natives include the vigilant mosquito (*Culex pervigilans*), a nocturnal species that is betrayed by its whine. It is found throughout New Zealand. Adult male mosquitoes feed on plant juices, and it is the female alone who takes blood to nourish the eggs in her abdomen. She lays her raft of eggs on wet mud or standing water, and the larvae that hatch out suspend themselves from the water's surface by the tip of the abdomen, breathing air through a siphon.

Trichoptera: caddisflies

At first glance, caddisflies look a little like dull, hairy moths and because they all look similar, specialists often group them by the type of cases in which the larvae live. These are netbuilding caddis, spiral caddis, hornycased caddis, stoneycased caddis and stick caddis. All caddisflies live near water and all their larvae are aquatic. There are around 8000 species worldwide and New Zealand has about 200, all but one native. The name caddis is believed to be a reference to the travelling cloth salesmen from the Middle Ages who pinned samples of cloth called 'cadices' to their coats, in a similar way to the self-adornment carried out by some caddises.

Marine caddis adult, Otago Harbour.

Marine caddis *Philanisus plebeius* 18 mm

Marine caddis larva, Otago Harbour.

Family Chathamiidae. **Maori** ngaro waiwai. The marine caddis is one of New Zealand's five marine caddis species and the most widespread, found throughout most of the country as well as in Australia. It is the only marine caddis that occurs in the South Island and on Stewart Island. The female lays her eggs in the body cavity of starfishes; the hatching larva lives on seaweed and also builds its larval case out of this material. The adult (see photo in introduction above) is active by night and by day rests in out-of-the-way locations. Other native marine caddis species include the Three Kings caddis (*Philanisus mataua*), and the Kermadec caddis (*P. fasciatus*).

Lepidoptera: butterflies and moths

Even those people who profess a dislike for 'bugs' usually admit to liking moths and butterflies, and there are probably more books written about this group, and the often rather strange people who collect them, than about all the other insect orders combined. The usual definitions of a butterfly as 'a brightly coloured, day-flying insect, which rests with its wings held upwards' and a moth as a 'dull, nocturnal insect which rests with its wings flat', just don't fly here. Many of our moths are diurnal and brightly coloured, and some often rest with their wings upright. A better way of telling them apart is by looking at their antennae (see page 9). Those of the butterflies are smooth with clubbed ends and those of moths are feathered. There are about 150,000 Lepidoptera species worldwide of which about 85 per cent are moths. In New Zealand there are about 2700 described species.

Common blue, Zizina labradus labradus, *female (see page 104).*

Monarch *Danaus plexippus* 85 mm

Family Nymphalidae. **Maori** kahuku. This conspicuous monarch is a self-introduced species that colonised New Zealand soon after European settlement. However, the fact that it has a Maori name indicates that it probably strayed here even in the pre-colonial era. It is found throughout the country, but occurs more commonly in warmer areas. There are some areas, both in Northland and the Bay of Plenty, where it gathers in small colonies in the colder months. Although the caterpillar browses on a number of species of plants, including (rather reluctantly) dogbane, pumpkin and the pepper tree, in order to pupate successfully it needs a variety of asclepiad plants (milkweeds), of which swan plant is the most common in gardens. The larva is conspicuous, striped black and yellow. Although the larvae are preyed upon by paper wasps and soldier bugs, and springbok mantises eat caterpillars and butterflies, enough pupate later in the season to enable the monarchs to survive. In Australia this species is called the Pacific wanderer.

Red admiral *Bassaris gonerilla gonerilla* 55 mm

Family Nymphalidae. **Maori** kahu kura. The red admiral is a widespread native butterfly that can be found anywhere in the country where its hosts, stinging nettles (*Urtica* species), occur, particularly ongaonga (*U. ferox*), a shrubby nettle. The larva feeds within the nettles, from inside a shelter formed from silk, spun from the mouth, and folded-over leaves. The flight of the adult is strong and direct, and red admirals can often be seen in late summer sunbathing on walls and rocks. Numbers of this butterfly have dropped off considerably in the decades following the introduction of parasitising ichneumons, particularly the whitespotted ichneumonid (*Ecthromorpha intricatoria*), and the red admiral has also been preyed on by the brown soldier bug (*Cermatulus nasalis*). Pupae are also parasitised by the wasp *Pteromalus puparum*, which was introduced to help control white butterfly. Another subspecies, *Bassaris gonerilla ida*, occurs in the Chathams. A similar-looking butterfly from the same family, and found in Europe, Asia and North America, is also called red admiral but is a different species, *Vanessa atalanta*.

Yellow admiral *Bassaris itea* 45 mm

Family Nymphalidae. **Maori** kahu kowhai. Unlike the closely related red admiral, the yellow admiral also occurs overseas, being found in Australia and the Loyalty Islands of New Caledonia. In New Zealand it is widespread throughout the three main islands from low to medium altitudes; however, unlike the red admiral, it has never been recorded from the Chatham Islands. Like the red admiral, the female lays her eggs on stinging nettles and she seeks out herbaceous soft-leaved nettles, such as *Urtica urens*, in late summer. The adult can often be seen, together with the red admiral, feeding from the introduced butterfly bush, *Buddleja davidii*, which is highly invasive and has become widespread.

LEPIDOPTERA

Family Nymphalidae. **Maori** pepe para hua. This attractive butterfly is an annual vagrant from Australia and in some years considerable numbers can be seen in New Zealand in late summer. Although it sometimes breeds here, it is not yet established but probably eventually will be. The adult flies fast and low to the ground and sometimes sunbathes flat on the ground, looking as though it has been run over. Its host plants include many garden daisies, such as the various *Helichrysum* species.

Boulder copper *Boldenaria boldenarum* 25 mm

Boulder copper, male. Note mauve colour and pronounced wing veins.

Boulder copper, female. Note blue spots around edge of wings.

Family Lycaenidae. **Maori** pepe para riki. The native boulder copper is found just about anywhere tussock grasses occur, and is most numerous in the South Island. As with the other coppers, ongoing research indicates that what was once regarded as a single species is probably a complex of many, and examining a series of this butterfly collected in different areas reveals a remarkable range of patterns and colours. The adult, one of New Zealand's smallest butterflies, is active on the wing from November through to March and its host plants are creeping

Boulder copper, caterpillar.

pohuehue (*Muehlenbeckia* species) and sorrel. The caterpillars are also variable in colour, ranging from green to red. This species was formerly known as *Lycaena boldenarum*.

101

Glade copper *Lycaena feredayi* 30 mm

Family Lycaenidae. **Maori** pepe para riki. The native glade copper is common along the shores of lakes, and along edges and clearings in forests, and it is from the latter habitat that it gets its name. It is

a highly variable species and it is likely that what was once deemed to be a single species will eventually prove to be many. As with the other coppers, the host plant for the glade copper is the creeping pohuehue (*Muehlenbeckia* species).

Common copper *Lycaena salustius* 34 mm

Common copper, male. Note pronounced double wing veins.

Common copper, female. Note faint blue spots around edge of wings.

Family Lycaenidae. **Maori** pepe para riki. This native butterfly is commonly found in coastal areas throughout the country, particularly where its host plants, the various larger-leaved *Muehlenbeckia* species, are found. The eggs are greenish-blue with white flecks and the hatching caterpillar is dark green with a distinct black dorsal line. Once pupation is complete, the butterfly lives for one to two weeks. One of the better places to look for it is among vegetation on, and abutting, sand dunes. Anecdotal evidence suggest that its caterpillars are suffering from parasitisation by the Asian paper wasp (*Polistes chinensis*; see page 127), and butterflies are not as abundant in the dunes as they once were.

103

Long-tailed blue *Lampides boeticus* 30 mm

Family Lycaenidae. The long-tailed blue arrived in New Zealand only in the 1960s, but has since spread throughout the North Island and also into Nelson and Marlborough. Overseas, it is probably the

most widespread of all butterfly species, as it ranges from Europe through Asia and Australia and into the Pacific. It is also found in parts of Africa. Its host plants are legumes, most commonly in New Zealand brooms, peas, beans, gorse and tree lucerne. In spring the female lays its white eggs singly on the flowers of these plants, and the larva pupates inside individual flowers, which wither and fall off, whereupon the butterfly emerges. Australians know this species as the peablue butterfly.

Common blue *Zizina labradus labradus* 25 mm

Family Lycaenidae. **Maori** pepe ao uri. The common blue is Australia's most common butterfly, and also one of New Caledonia's, but it became established here only when early colonists introduced its host plants, leguminous species such as pink and white clover and tree lucerne. Now, it is common in most open areas in the North Island and in the north and west of the South Island to around 1000 m. The male (pictured) is a stronger blue in colour. The female, a duller grey, seeks out its host plants and lays eggs on the leaves. Upon hatching, the larva is colourless and slug-like, becoming green once it starts foraging. In the south and east of the South Island, this subspecies is replaced by *Zizina labradus oxleyi*, which has more rounded forewings, a darker undersurface and a more definite pattern of spots.

104

White butterfly *Pieris rapae* 47 mm

Family Pieridae. **Maori** pepe ma. The white butterfly arrived in New Zealand from Europe at Napier in 1929, presumably in a cargo of vegetables, and from there it has spread throughout the country, even to the Chathams, and some individuals, presumably wind-blown, have even been noted on the

subantarctic islands. Its favoured host plants are cabbages, broccoli and cauliflower, along with the leaves of several other plants such as nasturtiums. In warmer parts of the country five generations a year are not unusual, but in colder areas two are the norm. Several insects have been introduced to control this pest, including a minute parasitic wasp, *Pteromalus puparum*, and a braconid wasp, *Apanteles glomeratus* (see page 128).

Black mountain ringlet *Percnodaimon merula* 45 mm

Brian Patrick

Family Satyridae. **Maori** pepe pouri. The native black mountain ringlet is often seen in summer months flying over subalpine and alpine vegetation throughout most of the South Island, except for parts of Central Otago. It sometimes strays into lower-altitude areas. The adult is diurnal, and its black wings serve as efficient heat attractors, a type of solar heating. The dun-coloured larva feeds on blue tussock (*Poa colensoi*) and several other related tussock species. The adult female does not deposit her eggs on vegetation but rather on adjoining rocks where the sun's heat assists in their hatching.

105

Dark coprosma carpet *Austrocidaria similata* 33 mm

Family Geometridae. This is one of the world's largest moth families, with about 20,000 species. About 300 species, some still undescribed, are found in New Zealand; most are endemic. The dark coprosma carpet is one of our more abundant moths. It is a day-flier and it is commonly seen in forested areas from November

to early March. It seeks out the various *Coprosma* species, such as the karamu, shining karamu, kanono and taupata, and the eggs once hatched develop into typical 'looper' caterpillars. There are a number of *Austrocidaria* species here, all of which look rather similar to this moth, and all of which use *Coprosma* species as their host trees.

Large striped carpet *Asaphodes clarata* 34 mm

Family Geometridae. **Maori** tawhana. The large striped carpet is a widespread day-flying moth that is common over tussock grasslands in both main islands in late summer and early autumn. Its host plants are the native buttercups (*Ranunculus* species). The adult rests with wings outstretched and can sometimes be spotted resting in the sun at favoured locales. The caterpillar is called a looper, or inchworm; since it has no prolegs in the middle of its body it is obliged to extend its forelegs out, then bring up the hind legs in an inverted 'U' shape. There are many geometrid moths in New Zealand but the *Asaphodes* species are among the most attractive; some are now becoming rarer and are listed as threatened species.

Silver fern looper *Chalastra aristarcha* 34 mm

Family Geometridae. The silver fern looper is common throughout the forests of the North Island from North Cape south to Wellington, and can be found almost anywhere its host plant, the silver fern or ponga (*Cyathea dealbata*), occurs. As this tree fern is rather scarce in the south, this probably explains the absence of this moth from the South Island. The genus has not been much studied, so little is known of its biology. Related species seem to have differing host plants: *Chalastra ochrea* is found on kowhai; *C. pellurgata* is associated with kanuka.

North Island lichen moth *Declana atronivea* 42 mm

Family Geometridae. This is a North Island species that is often found in forested areas, where it can, with difficulty, be spotted resting among lichen, which affords it camouflage. The larvae are just as hard to spot as they look very similar to bird droppings. The caterpillar eats foliage of five-finger trees. The related South Island lichen moth (*Declana egregia*) feeds on both the common and the mountain five-finger.

Cabbage tree moth *Epiphryne verriculata* 65 mm

Family Geometridae. **Maori** purehi ti. The native cabbage tree moth is widespread throughout the two main islands of New Zealand, at lower altitudes, wherever its host cabbage trees (*Cordyline* species) are found. When at rest this moth is very difficult to spot as the lines on its wings align with the veins on dead cabbage tree leaves. Presence of the moth is usually detected by the holes and notches chewed in the leaves of the host plant by the larvae. The larva is pale green in colour and is found in the crown of the cabbage tree, feeding on the tender leaves. A related species is the aristotelia looper (*Epiphryne xanthaspis*), which is found on wineberry, from the Volcanic Plateau southwards.

Striped orange underwing *Paranotoreas ferox* 22 mm

Family Geometridae. This lovely geometrid is restricted to alpine areas of the South Island, from Marlborough south to Central Otago, but it is more common on the eastern side of the main divide. Like the other *Paranotoreas* species, it is diurnal and can often be seen on sunny days sunbathing on rocks, although it can be quite difficult to spot as the colourful hind wings are covered by the dark forewings when the moth is resting. The larvae are believed to

Brian Patrick

feed on alpine herbs. Related, and similar, species are the orange underwing (*P. brephosata*) – a less distinctly marked geometrid which prefers lower altitudes – and the creekbed orange underwing (*P. zopyra*), which is smaller and more bluish in colour.

109

Green lichen tuft moth *Izatha peroneanella* 44 mm

Family Oecophoridae. This pretty native moth is to be found throughout most of the country, in December and January, but more generally in forested areas. The colour of the adult is variable, with some specimens appearing almost green. The female lays its eggs on the surface of dead branches of trees such as wineberry, and the larva then drills a tunnel into the branch. There are two related native species worthy of mention: the white lichen tuft moth (*Izatha picarella*), which although similar in pattern is of a somewhat darker colour; and the yellow litter moth (*Tingena armigerella*), which lacks distinctive patterning on its wings.

Arrowhead *Diasemia grammalis* 18 mm

Family Crambidae. The day-flying arrowhead frequents areas of low shrubbery and rank grasses at all altitudes up to alpine zones throughout New Zealand. The adult is frequently seen on the wing between April and October. It is a swift flier, darting about seeking out its host plants, the creeping pohuehue (*Muehlenbeckia* species). Although we seem to have only a single species from this genus in mainland New Zealand, there is another, *Diasemia ramburialis*, which appears to be restricted to the Kermadecs, and other *Diasemia* species are found in many parts of Europe and Asia. It gets its common name from the arrow-like markings on its forewings.

110

Puriri moth *Aenetus virescens* 135 mm

Family Hepialidae. **Maori** pepe tuna. The beautiful puriri moth is New Zealand's largest and heaviest moth. It is normally green, but blue and yellow individuals sometimes occur. It is widespread

throughout the North Island, but has not been reported from the South. The puriri moth has a two-stage larval history with the youngest larva initially feeding off bracket fungus on dead logs. In the second stage it burrows into host trees to feed on the inner bark and sapwood just under the bark. It closes off the burrow entrance once pupation begins, and here it spends up to six or more years. Despite its name, its caterpillars chew tunnels not only in puriri trees but also in putaputaweta, lacebark (houhere), wineberry and the various beech species and even in the introduced oak trees.

Swift moth *Wiseana cervinata* 56 mm

Family Hepialidae. **Maori** purehurehu. There are seven swift moths belonging to the genus *Wiseana*. Although native, several have adapted enthusiastically to the pastures cultivated by European settlers and their larvae are now major pests in farmland. *Wiseana cervinata* (pictured) is the most common and widespread species; *W. signata* is restricted to Nelson and coastal Marlborough; and *W. umbraculata* prefers soggy conditions, so is not of as much concern to farmers, although it can damage flaxes (*Phormium* species). The biology of the remaining four *Wiseana* species is not yet fully understood. Swift moths fly in October, November and December, scattering numerous eggs, which look like tiny buckshot over pasture. When these hatch in about three to five weeks, the larvae become voracious nocturnal eaters of grass and can quickly denude wide areas.

Gum emperor moth *Opodiphthera eucalypti* 110 mm

Gum emperor moth adult (top) and caterpillar (lower).

Family Saturniidae. This spectacular moth arrived from Australia in about 1938 and is now to be found wherever its host trees, the *Eucalyptus* species, occur. In Australia it is found from Tasmania to the Northern Territory and is relatively common. Here, partly because of parasitoids, it never occurs in any numbers, so its nuisance value is limited. The adult's hind wings have 'eye' markings, which, when flashed, startle predators. The adult does not eat, but the larva feeds on a variety of eucalyptus trees as well as on the pepper tree (*Schinus molle*). The caterpillar is large, fat and is coloured greenish-blue with yellow lateral stripes and blue spots. The adult moth appears in November and December, and this is the best time to look for it, in the vicinity of eucalyptus trees. It was formerly known as *Antheraea eucalypti*.

113

Silver Y moth *Chrysodeixis eriosoma* 38 mm

Family Noctuidae. **Maori** purehurehu. Although a native, this moth is widespread from India to New Zealand, but here it does not seem too common south of Christchurch. It gets its common name from a silver 'Y' marking on the adult's forewing, which the eagle-eyed can make out. It is often to be seen in late summer evenings harvesting nectar from flowers such as marigolds. The larva is green with thin, white lines becoming apparent as pupation nears. The caterpillar targets a wide range of fruits and vegetables, so it is of concern to gardeners. It attacks both the leaves and fruit of plants such as tomatoes, beans, potatoes, tamarillos, mint and passionfruit.

Spangled green owlet *Cosmodes elegans* 36 mm

Family Noctuidae. The spangled green owlet is an Australian moth that has now spread widely throughout the North and South Islands. It is particularly common in coastal areas in the late autumn when it is seeking out its host plants, lobelia and verbena. The caterpillar is smooth and green, and when it is ready to pupate it drops to the ground and buries itself in the soil. In Australia, where it is also very widespread, it is sometime called the green blotched moth. Its former scientific name was *Phalaena elegans*.

114

Northern wattle moth *Dasypodia cymatodes* 80 mm

Family Noctuidae. **Maori** para kori taua. The northern wattle moth is a heavy-bodied, nocturnal moth that originated in Australia and is now common throughout the North Island and in Nelson in the South Island. A related species, the moon moth, or southern wattle moth (*Dasypodia selenophora*), largely replaces it in the remainder of the South Island and on Stewart Island. The northern wattle moth occasionally arrived here before European settlement, but it was not until colonists planted its host trees, the *Acacia* or wattles, that it became established. The caterpillar is yellowish-brown with black dots and the adult moth emerges in late summer.

Grapevine moth *Phalaenoides glycinae* 55 mm

Family Noctuidae. The grapevine moth first arrived here from Australia in the early 1940s and is now well established throughout the north of the North Island. The adult could be confused with the magpie moth (*Nyctemera annulata*, see page 119), but the latter is somewhat smaller and has white spots on its forewings, while the grapevine moth has yellowish bars. Both species, however, are day fliers. As in Australia, where it is a serious pest, the grapevine moth here attacks both the vine foliage and the developing grapes. It also targets fuchsia and Virginia creeper. The caterpillar is quite striking, being green to yellowish-black, covered with broken longitudinal black

lines and spots and numerous hairy black tubercles. The anterior end is yellowish while the posterior is red.

Slender burnished brass *Thysanoplusia orichalcea* 38 mm

Family Noctuidae. This moth first appeared in New Zealand in Pukekohe in 1984 and has spread throughout most of the North Island. Overseas it is very widespread. Its alternative names all point to notoriety as a pest. These include the soybean looper, cabbage semi-looper and sunflower semi-looper. In New Zealand it attacks mostly lucerne, brassicas, carrots, soybeans and parsley. The eggs are laid in the spring and summer and the larva pupates in a cocoon of curled leaves. The larva is parasitised by the soybean looper parasitoid (*Copidosoma floridanum*; see page 129), a tiny wasp.

Northern pimelea owlet *Meterana pictula* 35 mm

Family Noctuidae. The native northern pimelea owlet occurs at all altitudes from sea level to subalpine and alpine scrubland in the central and eastern parts of the North Island and in Nelson, Marlborough and Westland in the South Island. The colourful larva feeds on the various species of native daphnes, or pinatoro. This is a nocturnal species, which rests with its wings folded tent-like over its body. In the remainder of the South Island it is replaced by the rather similar southern pimelea owlet (*Meterana meyricci*), which has paler hind wings. It is also sometimes called the pimelea cutworm.

Brian Patrick

117

Lichen bag moth *Cebysa leucotelus* 14 mm

Family Psychidae. **Maori** pu a raukatauri. The lichen bag moth is an Australian species that arrived here in the 1980s and is now well established. As with most other bag moths, the female is flightless, but this species is mobile and can be seen running on the ground. It sometimes wanders into houses, where because of its bright colours, it could be mistaken for a beetle or wasp. The male is a tiny cream-and-brown, diurnal moth and can fly. The larva constructs a somewhat ovoid bag made of silk spun from the jaws, incorporating bits of debris into the silk for camouflage. It remains in the bag until pupation, browsing on a diet of algae and lichens.

Common bag moth *Liothula omnivora* 35 mm

Family Psychidae. **Maori** pu a raukatauri. This is the most commonly found of our native bag moths, of which there are some 50 species. The larva constructs a long, silken, cone-shaped bag and moves around in it while feeding. The species is not too particular about its host tree, but can often be found on kanuka, manuka, tauhinu and neinei, as well as introduced tree and plant species, including feijoa, macrocarpa, willow, wattle, pine and broom; in 1955 an outbreak of this species caused considerable damage to radiata pines. The adult female is flightless and after pupating it remains within the bag, where it breeds and eventually dies. The dusky grey male is rarely seen.

Common bag moth larva.

Magpie moth *Nyctemera annulata* 40 mm

Family Arctiidae. **Maori** mokarakara. The magpie moth is a common, widespread native species that ranges throughout mainland New Zealand and can even be found on some of our subantarctic islands. It is a day-flying moth, rather similar to but smaller than the grapevine moth (see page 116). Although not a strong flier, the adult can often be seen on the wing between September and April. Children often call the caterpillar 'woolly bear' as it is covered with large blue spots, deep red lines and very obvious tufts of long black hair. Obviously distasteful to predators, the caterpillar spends the day feeding in full view. Its host plants are ragwort, groundsel, German ivy and cineraria. A very similar species, the Australian magpie moth (*Nyctemera amica*), has larger white spots, but as the two species often hybridise, telling them apart can be problematic.

Cinnabar moth *Tyria jacobaeae* 34 mm

Family Arctiidae. The very pretty cinnabar moth was introduced here from Britain in 1929 in an effort to control the pest plant ragwort (*Senecio jacobaea*), on which the black-and-orange-banded caterpillars feed. Although thousands of moths were imported, they were largely unsuccessful as biological controls. The adult is largely nocturnal but can sometimes be seen fluttering weakly in the daytime. It is reasonably common in the southern part of the North Island, particularly in the Wairarapa, and in Nelson and Marlborough in the South Island. Both caterpillars and adult moths are poisonous to birds.

Cinnabar moth caterpillars.

White plume moth *Pterophorus furcatalis* 25 mm

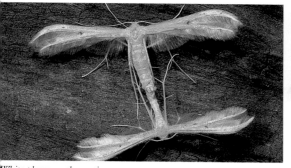

White plume moths mating.

Family Pterophoridae. **Maori** purerehuhu. New Zealand has around 20 plume moths, all rather similar and all native. The white plume moth adult is a delicate moth that holds its long, narrow wings at right angles to its body in a 'T' shape. When resting the wings are furled up rather like a closed umbrella but when flying they are extended like feathery plumes. The adult has long, thin 'deciduous' legs (they break off easily if handled) and is an indifferent flier. The lethargic larva feeds on *Pittosporum* species.

Brown plume moth *Platyptilia falcatalis* 25 mm

Family Pterophoridae. **Maori** purerehuhu. The brown plume moth is very similar in biology to the white plume moth (see previous entry), except that the host plants for the larva are koromiko (*Hebe salicifolia* and *H. stricta*). The adult holds its wings in a 'T' shape.

121

Currant clearwing *Synanthedon tipuliformis* 16 mm

Family Sesiidae. This species is the only representative of its family in New Zealand. The currant clearwing superficially resembles a wasp, which may help protect it from predators. Its host plants are black and red currants and gooseberries. As these plants are not tolerant of hot summers, they tend to be grown south of Hamilton in the North Island and in the South Island, thus limiting the range of this moth. It is a sun-loving, diurnal moth and although the wings are initially scaled, these fall off during the first flight. The adult female deposits its eggs on the foliage and upon hatching the larva drills into a branch.

Apple leafroller *Epiphyas postvittana* 25 mm

Family Tortricidae. **Maori** tikopa. Sometimes called the lightbrown apple moth, this Australian species was accidentally introduced

Brian Patrick

into New Zealand about 1891. The larva feeds on a wide variety of native and exotic plants and so is a pest in pip-fruit orchards, particularly apples. The larva is a fast mover and to make a secure refuge it rolls up leaves, securing them with silk produced from its mouth. A number of different wasp species and a tachinid fly are having a limited effect in controlling this moth. These include the tachinid fly *Trigonospila brevifacies* (see page 89), and the ichneumonids *Glabridorsum stokesii* (page 130) and *Xanthopimpla rhopaloceros* (page 132).

Hymenoptera: ants, bees and wasps

After the Coleoptera (beetles) the Hymenoptera is the second largest insect order. About 120,000 species have been named, with an estimated two to three times that number still to be classified. In New Zealand, there are an estimated 2000 to 3000 species. The Hymenoptera are defined as a holometabolous group (developing by metamorphosing from a distinct larval into a distinct adult stage). In sighted species, they have two pairs of membranous wings, with the larger wings connected to smaller hind wings by a series of hooks. The hooks are located on the front edge of the hind wing and they hook over the back edge of the forewing. Hymenoptera species are mostly thin or 'wasp'-waisted and always have an ovipositor, which is modified for stinging in the social bees and wasps and some ants. Many of New Zealand's species remain to be described.

Honey bee *Apis mellifera* 20 mm

Family Apidae. **Maori** pi honi. The honey bee arrived in New Zealand early in the period of European settlement. It has a highly organised social system, with the hive being made up of the queen, who alone lays all the eggs; the drones, who are stingless males whose duty it is to mate with the queen; and the thousands of sexless workers (which can sting), who keep the hive supplied with food (nectar and pollen). In the early 2000s, the *Varroa* mite, a serious pest which decimates hives, appeared in New Zealand, and now has spread throughout the North Island and has recently appeared in the South.

Bumblebee *Bombus terrestris* 25 mm

Bumblebees mating.

Family Apidae **Maori** pi rorohu Bumblebees were deliberately introduced from Britain in the 1880s to pollinate the flowers of red clover, a pasture crop. The proboscises of the native bees and the honey bee are too short to reach the nectar reward so they gave up on visiting flowers of red clovers. A number of bumblebee species were introduced and four became established here: *Bombus terrestris* (pictured), *B. hortorum*, *B. ruderatus* and *B. subterraneus*. As each species has a proboscis of a different length, they seek out different food plants and help in their pollination. All bumblebees except for the queen, which hibernates, die off in winter. In the spring the queen emerges and builds a nest, usually in a hole in the ground, but sometimes in trees or rock crevices. When each larva completes its development and emerges as an adult, it helps the queen feed later arrivals.

Native bee *Leioproctus* species 8 mm

Family Colletidae. **Maori** ngaro. The first species of native bees were described in 1853, although the bulk of research has been recent and 18 species, including that pictured here, are now in the process of being named. The bee pictured is a North Island species and is fairly uncommon. Much more likely to be encountered are *Leioproctus fulvescens*, which is also dark brown/black but clothed in dense golden yellow hairs, and found only in the South Island; and *L. metallicus*, which is more robust and shinier. The native bees are solitary nesters, although you may find many nests together in an area with suitable substrate, giving the appearance of a colony. The different species have preferences for nesting substrate. *L. fulvescens* needs fine-grained ground whereas *L. metallicus* likes coastal sand above high-tide level. The bees often dig tunnels in clay banks, so can often be seen in road cuttings. Although they do not produce honey, the native bees are important pollinators of plants.

German wasp *Vespula germanica* 19 mm

Family Vespidae. **Maori** wahipi. The German wasp was accidentally introduced into New Zealand during the Second World War and is now found in urban, rural and coastal areas of the North and South Islands. Like the honey bee it is a social insect and workers build large paper nests in trees, under roofs, or in holes in the ground. These they construct from a sort of papier-mâché material that is produced by chewing up wood scrapings. The larvae are fed on flies and caterpillars, which the workers hunt down. Wasps are a nuisance in orchards and vineyards and they can deliver a nasty sting. An alternative Maori name for the wasp is pi Waikato, which refers to this rugby team's black-and-yellow colours.

Common wasp *Vespula vulgaris* 18 mm

Family Vespidae. **Maori** wahipi. This European wasp was first noticed in New Zealand in the 1920s, but did not really get established until the 1970s, when the population rocketed. It is now established in many parts of the country and is particularly common in forested areas; in beech forests the population sometimes reaches plague proportions. As it competes for the honeydew excreted by the sooty beech scale that is important in the diet of native birds, in particular that of kaka, tui and bellbirds, it is of concern to conservationists. The nests occasionally can be up to two to three metres across, much larger than any found in its native Europe.

Asian paper wasp *Polistes chinensis* 14 mm

Family Vespidae. **Maori** pi whero. This wasp from Asia first established itself around Auckland in the late 1970s, but it has spread as far south as Nelson and Blenheim in the South Island. Nests are umbrella-shaped constructions built by the wasps in protected areas such as under eaves. The larvae are fed small insects. A related species, the Austral-

Asian paper wasp adults at nest.

ian paper wasp (*Polistes humilis humilis*) arrived here much earlier, being seen around Hokianga in the 1880s. It is mainly confined to the warmer areas from the Bay of Plenty north. It differs from the Asian paper wasp in having a brown abdomen. Both species can inflict a painful sting.

European potter wasp *Ancistrocerus gazella* 10 mm

Family Eumenidae. The European potter wasp first arrived in New Zealand at Auckland in 1987, but is now found as far south as Dunedin and Central Otago. It is a solitary nester, unlike its infamous cousins, the German wasps and the common wasps, and it seems to have a preference for drill or nail holes in buildings as sites for nest construction. In these the adult female builds cells into which she deposits a single egg. The hole is then stocked with paralysed caterpillars, which the wasp larva eats once hatched. As it prefers the caterpillars of leafroller moths, which are a pest in orchards, it is probably more beneficial than harmful.

127

White butterfly braconid wasp *Apanteles glomeratus* 3 mm

Family Braconidae. Braconid wasps prey on a variety of insect including butterflies, beetles, flies and aphids, but this species preferred victim is the white butterfly. It was introduced from England and the United States and is found throughout New Zealand. The female lays its eggs in the white butterfly larvae When fully developed, the wasp larva (pictured) chews through the body wall of its host to emerge and spin its distinctive yellow silken cocoon. Inside this, the larvae pupate at the same time together. On average 30 wasp larvae emerge from a single butterfly larva. A relative, *Apanteles ruficrus*, deliberately introduced from Pakistan in 1972, is a valuable biological control, as it preys on about 50 species of moth caterpillars. Another relative, *A. circumscriptus* was introduced in 1957 to control the oak leafminer (*Lithocolletis messaniella*).

Soybean looper parasitoid *Copidosoma floridanum* 1 mm

Family Encyrtidae. Widespread overseas, this minute wasp was introduced from Australia and it is now found throughout the North Island and as far south as Mid Canterbury. As its name indicates, it parasitises the caterpillar of the slender burnished brass, or soybean looper (*Thysanoplusia orichalcea*), a moth whose caterpillars are garden pests as they attack potatoes, carrots and a number of other vegetables. It also attacks the caterpillars of the silver Y moth (page 114). The adult female wasp lays a single egg in the moth's egg. The egg floats around in the cavity of the caterpillar that hatches, then undergoes division to produce up to 2000 embryos (a process called polyembryony). The wasp larva undergoes most of its development once the host caterpillar is almost fully grown. Because of this, the wasp needs to time its egg laying to synchronise with the breeding of the moth. As the larvae do not consume the caterpillar until it is almost fully grown, its use as a control is of limited value.

Leafroller ichneumonid *Glabridorsum stokesii* 7 mm

Family Ichneumonidae. The leafroller ichneumonid wasp was first introduced from Australia in the late 1960s and 1970s to attack and control leafroller moths in orchards, and is now well established throughout the North Island and in the top of the South. The adult female lays a single egg on the leafroller caterpillar, but should another egg be laid by another wasp, the first larva to hatch bites these other eggs, and thus eliminates any competition. Although primarily a parasite of leafrollers, this wasp is also known to attack the caterpillars of codling moths and oriental fruit moths. All ichneumonids have delicate, slender bodies, with long legs and antennae.

Orange ichneumonid *Netelia producta* 20 mm

Family Ichneumonidae. The orange ichneumonid wasp is found throughout the North Island, as well as in parts of the South Island. Sometimes called the red soldier wasp or red jacket, it also occurs in Australia and in parts of Indonesia. Its prey is not well known, but is believed to be the caterpillars of noctuid moths, which are better known as armyworm caterpillars, a serious pest in pastures. The adult wasp can sting.

Lemon tree borer parasite *Xanthocryptus novozealandicus* 10 mm

Family Ichneumonidae. **Maori** ngaro whiore. This ichneumonid superficially resembles the leafroller ichneumonid (see page 130), but it is usually somewhat larger. Although a widespread New Zealand native, it is also found in Australia and Papua New Guinea. The female eats the larvae of longhorn beetles (Cerambycidae), but it is of importance to horticulturalists because it seeks out the larvae of the lemon tree borer (see page 64), which is a significant pest in citrus orchards and vineyards. The peak period for egg laying is in March, and the female drives her ovipositor through the wood and into the larva to lay her eggs.

Yellowbanded leafroller parasitoid *Xanthopimpla rhopaloceros* 8 mm

Family Ichneumonidae. Now widespread throughout the North Island, and in Nelson and Marlborough in the South, this ichneumonid wasp was introduced from Australia in the 1960s and 1970s as a biological control for the larvae of leafroller moths, although it has a wide range of hosts. It locates the host pupae with a minimum of searching. Pupae concealed in rolled leaves are detected and parasitised through the leaf.

Whitespotted ichneumonid *Ecthromorpha intricatoria* 22 mm

Family Ichneumonidae. This wasp was self-introduced from Australia during the First World War, and is now widely distributed throughout mainland New Zealand. The adult female lays eggs in the pupae of a number of Lepidoptera species, including pests such as tomato fruitworm, green looper, magpie moth (see page 119) common bag moth (page 118) and the gum emperor moth (page 113). On the other hand, it also attacks harmless butterflies like the red admiral (page 98), and limits the spread of the cinnabar moth (page 120), which was introduced to control ragwort.

Praying mantis parasitoid *Eupelmus antipoda* 3 mm

Family Eupelmidae. This tiny wasp is also found in Australia but no one knows if its presence in New Zealand is natural or if it was accidentally introduced. It parasitises the eggs of the New Zealand praying mantis (*Orthodera novaezealandiae*; see page 29). It is a representative of a very large wasp group, whose species are generally minute. So far around 22,000 species have been described but there could be as many as 500,000. Evidence suggests that the chalcid wasps make up about 10 per cent of all insect species. Chalcid wasps is the common name for the superfamily Chalcidoidea, composed of many families, of which Eupelmidae is but one.

Black cockroach hunter *Tachysphex nigerrimus* 11 mm

Family Sphecidae. **Maori** ngaro wiwi. The black cockroach hunter is a native species that is widespread throughout mainland New Zealand. The adult generally nests in areas of sand, silt or fine shingle, such as those provided by river-banks, and here it constructs a simple burrow above the flood level. It specialises in hunting for the small native *Celatoblatta* cockroaches (pictured; see also page 24), in particular the species *C. undulivitta*. After stinging and paralysing them, the female cockroach hunter drags them back to her burrow. Three cockroach nymphs are left for each wasp egg.

133

Southern ant *Monomorium antarcticum* 3 mm

Family Formicidae. **Maori** upokorua. There are about 40 ant species known from New Zealand, but only 11 are endemic, the rest introduced, and this native species is by far the most common and the most widely distributed, being found throughout all three main islands as well as on the Chathams and the Three Kings. It also utilises a wide range of habitats, from sand dunes to forests and tussock lands, and lives in tunnels. This omnivorous ant occurs in a range of colours from black to red. Ant colonies have a caste or social system, rather similar to that of bees, with workers and usually only one queen.

Whitefooted house ant *Technomyrmex albipes* 2 mm

Family Formicidae. **Maori** poko. After the southern ant (see previous entry), the next most commonly encountered ant species in New Zealand is the introduced whitefooted house ant, a cosmopolitan species that is widespread in many parts of the North and northern South Islands, with new colonies recently appearing in parts of Canterbury. It is the most common species to enter houses but also builds nests in rotting trees where it can force out native ant species. Colonies can have several queens and number several thousand members. In autumn, large swarms of winged adults often occur when they leave their home nest to form new colonies, particularly in the Auckland area.

Glossary

Abdomen the hinder part of an insect; comprises up to 11 segments, and used for the storage of fat and containing the bulk of the digestive and excretory systems.

Ametabolous referring to insects in which a nymph hatches from the egg as a miniature version of the adult, periodically moulting its exoskeleton until reaching maturity.

Antennae appendage or 'feelers' on the insect's head.

Caterpillar larva of a moth or butterfly.

Cerci pair of appendages on the last segment of the abdomen.

Chrysalis the pupa of a butterfly.

Class major division of a phylum.

Cocoon the outer protective covering around a pupa.

Dimorphic a species where sexes differ either in form or colour.

Dorsal of, on or near the back.

Elytra (singular **elytron**) the hard outer wing cases in beetles.

Endemic native and restricted to a certain area.

Exoskeleton outer hard casing, and the membranes between, in arthropods.

Exuvia (plural **exuviae**) nymph 'skin' (e.g. of cicada) that is the remains of the exoskeleton left behind after a moult.

Family rank below an order and above a genus.

Genus (plural **genera**) group of closely related species.

Grub larva of a beetle.

Haltere modified hind wing of flies which oscillates and provides sensory input on changes in flight path.

Hemimetabolous referring to insects in which a nymph hatches from the egg as a miniature, wingless version of the adult, gradually becoming more like the adult with each successive moult.

Holometabolous insects that go through four stages: egg, larva, pupa and finally the adult that hatches from the pupa. Each stage is quite dissimilar to that succeeding it.

Honeydew sweet, sticky substance excreted by aphids.

Host the insect or animal that a parasite lives on or feeds on.

Instar the stage in the development of an insect between any two successive moults.

Invertebrate creature lacking a backbone.

Labium lower lip.

Labrum upper lip.

Larva (plural **larvae**) the stage between egg and pupa of those insects that undergo complete metamorphosis.

Maggot larva of a fly.

Mandibles jaw-like mouthparts, used for chewing or crushing.

Maxillae mouthparts that lie behind the mandibles and are generally used for holding and manipulating food.

Metamorphosis development from egg to adult through a series of different stages.

Moult when one stage of a larva or nymph sheds its skin and the next stage emerges.

Nymph the larva(e) of hemimetabolous insects.

Ocelli simple eyes.

Ommatidia hexagonal facets in compound eyes.

Ootheca the egg case of mantises.

Order rank below a class and above a family.

Ovipositor the egg-laying apparatus of an adult female Orthopteran.

Parasite insect or animal that lives in or on another species of insect or animal (known as its host).

Parthenogenesis reproduction by an unfertilised female; reproduction without the need for mating.

Phylum (plural **phyla**) the rank below kingdom comprising a class or classes and subordinate taxa.

Predator an insect or animal that catches and eats other insects or animals (known as its prey).

Proboscis a tube-like mouthpart for sucking up liquids.

Pupa the stage between larva and adult of those insects that undergo complete metamorphosis.

Pupate when a larva changes into a pupa.

Rostrum modified mouthparts of Hemiptera that enable them to pierce the skins of plants or animals and to suck up the sap or blood they use as food.

Species a population of insects which share similar characteristics and which tend to produce infertile offspring if they mate with unrelated species.

Spiracle valve through which air enters the insect respiratory system.

Stinger a modified ovipositor.

Subspecies a form of a species consistently showing different features and with a separate distribution range.

Taxonomy theory and practice of classifying organisms into hierarchical groups known as taxa (singular taxon).

Tegmina toughened forewings (e.g. of earwigs).

Territory any defended area or place.

Thorax a muscle-filled box to which the wings (where present) and legs are attached.

Tympanum a structure in the abdomen of cicadas used for hearing and producing sound.

Ventral underside of body.

Further Reading

Child, J. & P., 1974, *New Zealand Dictionary of Biology*, Fontana Periwinkle.

Crowe, A., 2002, *Which New Zealand Insect?*, Penguin.

Dale, P., 1992, *A Houseful of Strangers*, HarperCollins.

Gibbs, G., 1998, *New Zealand Weta*, Reed.

Grant, E.A., 1999, *An Illustrated Guide to Some New Zealand Insect Families*, Manaaki Whenua Press.

Hudson, G.V., 1934, *New Zealand Beetles and their Larvae*, Ferguson & Osborne.

Meads, M., 1990, *Forgotten Fauna*, DSIR Publishing.

Miller, D. (revised by A.K. Wilson), 1984, *Common Insects in New Zealand*, Reed.

Parkinson, B., 2001, *Common Insects of New Zealand*, Reed Books.

Parkinson, B. & Patrick, B., 2000, *Butterflies and Moths of New Zealand*, Reed.

Peat, N. & Patrick, B., 1995, *Wild Dunedin*, University of Otago Press.

Peat, N. & Patrick, B., 1999, *Wild Central*, University of Otago Press.

Pendergrast, J.G. & Cowley, D.R., 1966, *Fresh Water Insects of New Zealand*, Collins.

Rowe, R., 1987, *The Dragonflies of New Zealand*, Auckland University Press.

Salmon, J.T., 1991, *The Stick Insects of New Zealand*, Reed.

Williams, H.W., 1921, *A Dictionary of the Maori Language*, Government Printer.

Index

Notes